snags and

A PRACTICAL GUIDE TO EVERYDAY ELECTRICAL PROBLEMS

Part 2
wiring
systems

The NICEIC

The National Inspection Council for Electrical Installation Contracting is a non-profit making organization set up to protect users of electricity against the hazards of unsafe and unsound electrical installations. The NICEIC is supported by all sectors of the electrical industry, approvals and research bodies, consumer interest organizations, the electricity supply industry, professional institutes and institutions, regulatory bodies, other professional bodies, trade and industry associations and federations, trade unions and local and central Government.

The NICEIC is the electrical contracting industry's independent voluntary regulatory body for electrical safety matters and each year publishes a Roll of around 10,500 Approved Contractors.

The NICEIC is accredited by the United Kingdom Accreditation Service (UKAS) to EN 45011 - *General requirements for bodies operating product certification systems* for its Approved Contractor scheme.

Published by:
NICEIC
Warwick House, Houghton Hall Park, Houghton Regis, Dunstable Bedfordshire LU5 5ZX
tel: 01582 531000,   fax: 01582 531010,   www.niceic.com

ISBN 0-9531058 9 X

Wiring Systems   **snags and solutions** © NICEIC

Snags and Solutions

Preface

What are the changes to the colours of fixed wiring?

The changes to the colour identification of conductors in fixed wiring are introduced, amongst other things, by Amendment No 2 to BS 7671 which was published on 31 March 2004. The new colours are the harmonized colours. The changes are effective from that day. However, up until 1 April 2006, it is permitted to continue to wire new installations in the present colours to use up existing stocks of cable. It is not permitted to wire a new installation using a mixture of the old and the new colours. One or the other must be used; but not both.

The Regulations cited in the following explanation are taken from Amendment no 2 of BS 7671.

The new colours: Single-phase

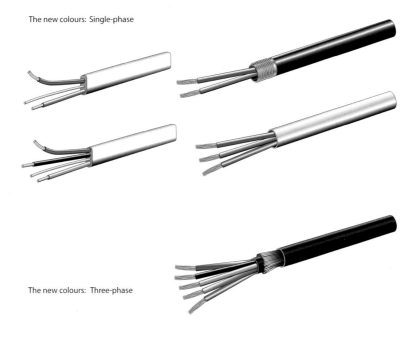

The new colours: Three-phase

SINGLE-PHASE INSTALLATIONS

The traditional colours of red and black for the phase and neutral conductors are replaced by the familiar colours of brown and blue (Regulations 514-03-01 and 514-04 refer). A neutral conductor, where identified by colour, must be identified by the colour blue (Regulation 514-04-01) and protective conductors remain green-and-yellow (Regulation 514-04-02).

New single-phase installations

A new installation should be wired in the colours of brown, blue and green-and-yellow.

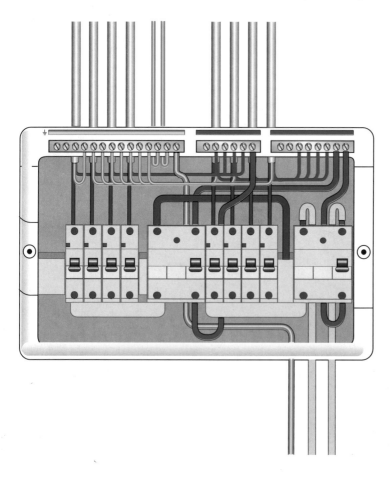

Switch wires.

Where a twin-and-earth cable with brown and blue conductors is used as a switch drop, both insulated conductors are phase conductors and the blue conductor must be suitably marked at its terminations. Such marking will normally be accomplished by brown sleeving.

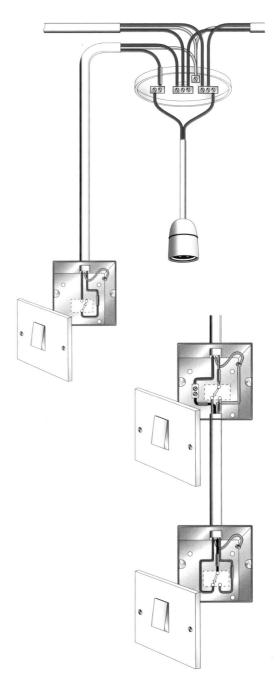

Intermediate and two-way switch wires.

Where a three-core and earth flat cable with cores coloured brown, black and grey is used as a switch wire and all three conductors are phase conductors, the black and grey conductors must, once again, be suitably marked and this will normally be realised by using brown sleeving.

Extensions, alterations or repairs to an existing single-phase installation

An extension, alteration or repair to an existing installation should be wired in the colours of brown, blue, and green-and-yellow.

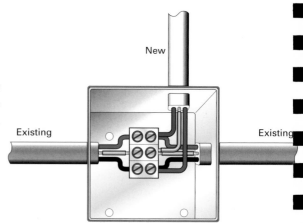

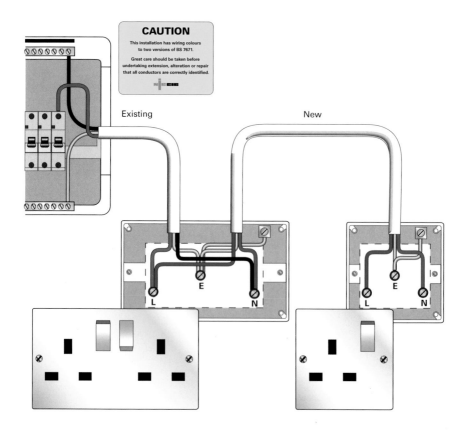

CAUTION

This installation has wiring colours to two versions of BS 7671.

Great care should be taken before undertaking extension, alteration or repair that all conductors are correctly identified.

Identification requirements - single-phase

At the wiring interface(s), providing:

- the existing cables are correctly identified by the colours of red for phase conductor and black for neutral conductor, and,

- the new cables are correctly identified by the colours of brown for phase conductor and blue for neutral conductor,

then the extension, alteration or repair can be considered to be unambiguously marked and further marking at the interface would not be necessary (Regulation 514-01-03 refers).

At the distribution board(s) or consumer unit(s)

If an extension, alteration or repair is made to an installation such that both brown & blue and red & black cables are present, a warning notice must be affixed at or near the appropriate distribution board or consumer unit with the following wording (Regulation 514-14-01 refers):

CAUTION

This installation has wiring colours to two versions of BS 7671.

Great care should be taken before undertaking extension, alteration or repair that all conductors are correctly identified.

THREE-PHASE INSTALLATIONS

The traditional colours of red, yellow and blue for the phase conductors and black for the neutral conductor are replaced by the colours of brown, black and grey for the phase conductors and blue for the neutral conductor. Protective conductors remain green-and-yellow (Regulations 514-03-01, 514-04-01 and 514-04-02 refer).

New three-phase installations

A new installation should be wired in the colours of brown, black and grey for the phase conductors and blue for the neutral conductor. The protective conductors remain green-and-yellow.

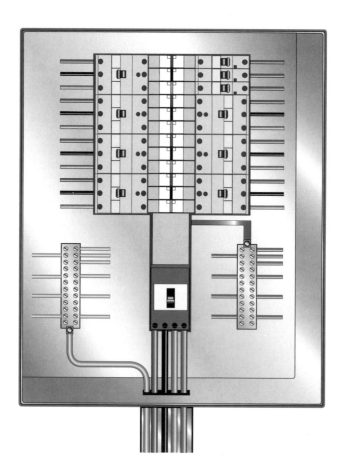

Extensions, alterations or repairs to an existing three-phase installation

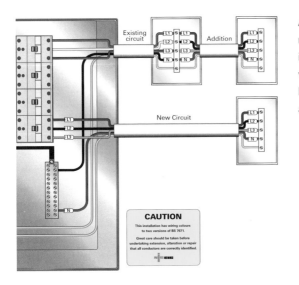

An extension, alteration or repair to an existing installation should be wired in the colours of brown, black, grey & blue, and green-and-yellow.

CAUTION

This installation has wiring colours to two versions of BS 7671.

Great care should be taken before undertaking extension, alteration or repair that all conductors are correctly identified.

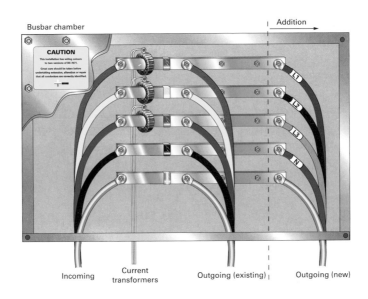

Identification requirements - three-phase installations

At the wiring interface(s), where an extension, alteration or repair is made with cable to the new colours to a three-phase installation wired in the old colours, unambiguous identification is required at the interface (Regulation 514-01-03 refers).

Neutral conductors, where identified by colour, must be identified by the colour blue (Regulation 514-04-01 refers). Old and new phase conductors should be fitted with sleeves marked L1, L2 and L3 and neutral conductors should be fitted with sleeves marked N to avoid any possibility of confusion.

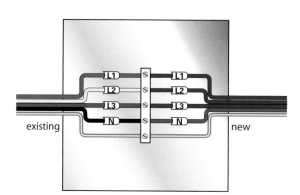

A permitted alternative arrangement is to use three single cores with insulation of the same colour but unambiguous identification must be provided at the terminations. This could be achieved by using numbering or lettering (Regulation 514-05-01 refers).

At the distribution board(s)

If an extension, alteration or repair is made to an installation such that both red, yellow, blue, black and brown, black, grey, blue are present, a warning notice must be affixed at or near the appropriate distribution board or consumer unit with the following wording:

> **CAUTION**
>
> **This installation has wiring colours to two versions of BS 7671.**
>
> **Great care should be taken before undertaking extension, alteration or repair that all conductors are correctly identified.**
>
>

Regulation 514-01-03

Except where there is no possibility of confusion, unambiguous marking shall be provided at the interface between conductors identified in accordance with these Regulations and conductors identified to previous versions of the Regulations. Appendix 7 gives guidance on how this can be achieved.

Regulation 514-03-01

Except where identification is not required by Regulation 514-06, cores of cables shall be identified by:

(i)   colour as required by Regulation 514-04 and /or

(ii) lettering and/or numbering as required by Regulation 514-05.

Regulation 514-03-02

Every core of a cable shall be identifiable at its terminations and preferably throughout its length.

Binding and sleeves for indentification purposes shall comply with BS 3858 where appropriate.

Regulation 514-04-01

Where a circuit includes a neutral or mid-point conductor identified by colour, the colour used shall be blue.

Regulation 514-04-02

The bi-colour combination green-and-yellow shall be used exclusively for identification of a protective conductor and this combination shall not be used for any other purposes.

Single-core cables that are coloured green-and-yellow throughout their length shall only be used as a protective conductor and shall not be over marked at their terminations, except as permitted by Regulation 514-04-03.

In this combination one of the colours shall cover at least 30 % and at most 70 % of the surface being coloured, while the other colour shall cover the remainder of the surface.

A bare conductor or busbar used as a protective conductor shall be identified, where necessary, by equal green-and-yellow stripes, each not less than 15 mm and not more than 100 mm wide, close together, either throughout the length of the conductor or in each compartment and unit and at each accessible position. If adhesive tape is used, it shall be bi-coloured.

Regulation 514-04-04

Other conductors shall be identified by colour in accordance with Table 51.

Regulation 514-05-01

The lettering or numbering system applies to identification of individual conductors and of conductors in a group. The identification shall be clearly legible and durable. All numerals shall be in strong contrast to the colour of the insulation. The identification shall be given in letters or Arabic numerals. In order to avoid confusion, unattached numerals 6 and 9 shall be underlined.

Regulation 514-06-01

Identification by colour or marking is not required for:

(i) concentric conductors of cables

(ii) metal sheath or armour of cables when used as a protective conductor

(iii) bare conductors where permanent identification is not practicable

(iv) extraneous-conductive-parts used as a protective conductor

(v) exposed-conductive-parts used as a protective conductor.

Regulation 514-14-01

If wiring alterations or additions are made to an installation such that some of the wiring complies with 514-04 but there is also wiring to previous versions of these Regulations, a warning notice shall be affixed at or near the appropriate distribution board with the following wording:

CAUTION

**This installation has wiring colours to two versions of BS 7671.
Great care should be taken before undertaking extension,
alteration or repair that all conductors are correctly identified.**

TABLE 51 - Identification of conductors

Function	Colour	Alpha numeric
Protective conductors	Green-and-yellow	
Functional earthing conductor	Cream	
a.c. power circuit[1]		
Phase of single-phase circuit	Brown	L
Neutral of single- or three-phase circuit	Blue	N
Phase 1 of three-phase a.c. circuit	Brown	L1
Phase 2 of three-phase a.c. circuit	Black	L2
Phase 3 of three-phase a.c. circuit	Grey	L3
Two-wire unearthed d.c. power circuit		
Positive of two-wire circuit	Brown	L+
Negative of two-wire circuit	Grey	L-
Two-wire earthed d.c. power circuit		
Positive (of negative earthed) circuit	Brown	L+
Negative (of negative earthed) circuit [2]	Blue	M
Positive (of positive earthed) circuit [2]	Blue	M
Negative (of positive earthed) circuit	Grey	L-
Three-wire d.c. power circuit		
Outer positive of two-wire circuit derived from three-wire system	Brown	L+
Outer negative of two-wire circuit derived from three-wire system	Grey	L-
Positive of three-wire circuit	Brown	L+
Mid-wire of three-wire circuit [2][3]	Blue	M
Negative of three-wire circuit	Grey	L-
Control circuits, ELV and other applications		
Phase conductor	Grey	L

Brown		Orange		White
Black		Yellow		Pink, or
Red		Violet		Turquoise

Function	Colour	Alpha numeric
Neutral or mid-wire [4]	Blue	N or M

NOTES:
[1] Power circuits include lighting circuits.
[2] M identifies either the mid wire of a three-wire d.c. circuit, or the earthed conductor of a two-wire earthed dc circuit.
[3] Only the middle wire of three-wire circuits may be earthed.
[4] An earthed PELV conductor is blue.

snags and solutions © NICEIC

Guide to how to use this book

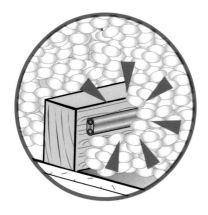

In these books of Snags and Solutions, a red circle on the left hand page illustrates the snag. Red triangles may be used to draw attention to what exactly is going wrong.

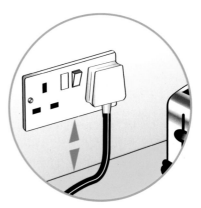

The green circle, generally on the right-hand page, illustrates the solution.

An important addition to your toolbox.

Snags Part 1 features the 50 most commonly-encountered earthing and bonding dilemmas. Explanations range from the different concepts of earthing and bonding to what to do with the kitchen sink.

This invaluable source of information can be obtained from NICEIC Sales at Warwick House, Houghton Hall Park, Houghton Regis, Dunstable LU5 5ZX.

Call us now on 01582 539700.

Index

▶ Snag 9 **Two-way switching using the cpc**
Circuit protective conductors of flat twin and earth cables
should not be used for any other purposes

▶ Snag 10 **Electrical enclosures outdoors**
Electrical enclosures, such as junction boxes and luminaires,
located outdoors are susceptible to water entry

▶ Snag 11 **Direct burying of cables**
Armoured or metal sheathed cables may be buried in the
ground but suitable precautions must be taken

▶ Snag 12 **Strain at glands of armoured cables**
A cable must properly fixed and supported throughout its
length. In most cases, an armoured cable gland should not be
used as a means of support

▶ Snag 13 **Unexpected joint box**
An 'unexpected' joint box should be avoided, wherever possible

▶ Snag 14 **Bending radii of cables**
A cable may be damaged by being bent to a radius smaller than
a given value

▶ Snag 15 **Enclosure of cores of sheathed cables**
The cores of a cable from which the sheath has been removed
must be properly enclosed

▶ Snag 16 **Supply to a smoke alarm**
BS 5839-6 (1995) gives recommendations for the supply to a
mains-powered smoke alarm in a dwelling

▶ Snag 17 **Cables at a junction box**
Circuit protective conductors should not be terminated outside a
junction box

▶ Snag 45 **Moulded connector strips and blocks**
Care must be taken to ensure a proper connection is made when moulded connector strips and blocks are used

▶ Snag 46 **Cable loops at motors**
Unsupported loops of cable at motors may be subject to vibrational stress

▶ Snag 47 **Green goo**
Green goo is a phenomena sometimes encountered in electrical installations constructed in the late 1960s

▶ Snag 48 **Electromagnetic effects at ferrous enclosures**
The conductors of an a.c. circuit entering a steel enclosure must not be separated by ferromagnetic material

▶ Snag 49 **Slotted trunking and ducting**
Slotted trunking or ducting is primarily intended for panel wiring

▶ Snag 50 **Temperature rise in mineral insulated cables**
Temperature rises in mineral insulated metal sheathed (MIMS) cables can be high enough to cause burns and deterioration of the insulation of other equipment such as accessories or pvc cables with which they may be in contact

▶ Snag 51 **Switch drop cables**
Switch drop cables must be properly identified

▶ Snag 52 **Identification of conductors in a swa cable**
Where a 3-core steel wire armoured (swa) cable is selected for use in a single-phase circuit, the conductors must be properly identified

▶ Snag 53 **Conductors must be correctly identified**
Conductors must be correctly identified by colour or alphanumerically to avoid confusion when the installation is repaired, extended or modified at a later date

Index

Socket-outlet positions

Plug-in appliances must be able to be easily and safely connected and disconnected.

Snag 1

If there is insufficient height between the socket-outlet and the finished floor of an office or a work surface in a kitchen, danger can result from the plug being forced in and out and from the flexible cord being squeezed or sharply bent.

Solution

snag **1**

Skirting trunking should itself be of sufficient height or the trunking should be raised above the finished floor screed. In either case allowance should be made for thick linoleum, tiles, wood block floors or carpet on underlay which could be laid later.

A socket-outlet must be mounted at a sufficient height above a work surface such that the socket-outlet, the plug and the flexible cord will not be damaged.

It is not acceptable to overcome the problem described above by inverting socket-outlets which are not designed for mounting upside down. In some circumstances this would result in a tripping hazard from a looped flex.

Regulation 553-01-06

A socket-outlet on a wall or similar structure shall be mounted at a height above the floor or any working surface to minimize the risk of mechanical damage to the socket-outlet or to an associated plug and its flexible cord which might be caused during insertion, use or withdrawal of the plug.

Pvc plasticiser

Pvc cables should not be allowed to come into contact with polystyrene.

Snag 2

The sheath of a pvc-sheathed cable can become sticky and soft to the touch, and eventually becomes hard and brittle, if installed where it is in contact with expanded polystyrene.

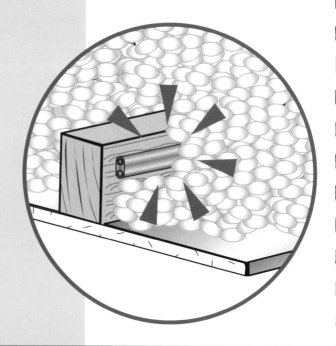

Solution

To comply with the requirements of the Regulations, contact between pvc cable sheaths and polystyrene must be avoided by design, or cable sheaths must be separated from polystyrene by an inert barrier such as pvc conduit or trunking.

Pvc cables suffer few defects and, provided they are correctly selected and carefully installed, will give reliable service.

Expanded polystyrene is sometimes used to insulate lofts and other parts of buildings, either in sheets or in granular form.

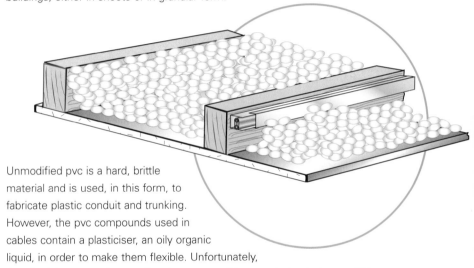

Unmodified pvc is a hard, brittle material and is used, in this form, to fabricate plastic conduit and trunking. However, the pvc compounds used in cables contain a plasticiser, an oily organic liquid, in order to make them flexible. Unfortunately, the plasticiser can migrate when in contact with expanded polystyrene. This process of migration is accelerated by heat arising from the passage of current down the cable, defects such as overloading or loose connections or high ambient temperatures such as may occur in a loft. As the plasticiser migrates, the sheath of a pvc-sheathed cable initially becomes sticky and soft to the touch and, eventually, becomes hard and brittle.

Regulation 522-05-03

Materials liable to cause mutual or individual deterioration or hazardous degradation shall not be placed in contact with each other.

Cord grips

Cord grips, where provided, must clamp firmly on to the sheath of the cable.

Snag 3

If the sheath of a cable is not properly engaged in the cord grip provided, the cores can become exposed, the connections can be stressed and there will be an increased risk of electric shock.

Snags encountered with cord grips include:

- Cord grip not used

- Cord grip clamped on insulation of conductors and not on sheath. This particular deficiency is often seen with plugs.

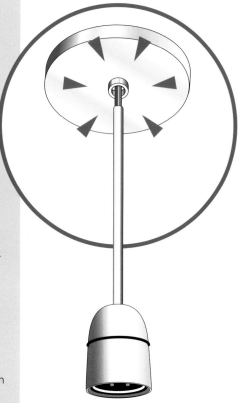

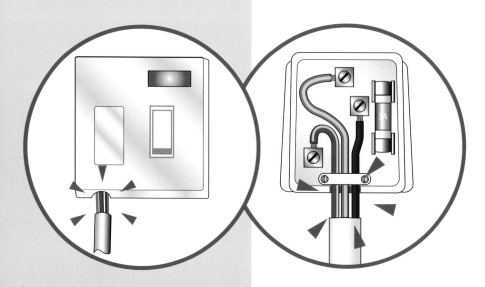

Solution

Cable terminations must be made without imposing mechanical strain on the terminal (Regulation 526-01-01 refers). To enable installers to meet this requirement, cord grip devices are incorporated in accessories such as ceiling roses, flexible cord outlet plates, cooker control units, cental heating outlet plates and plugs. It is essential that cord grips are correctly used.

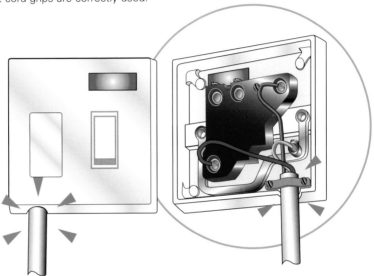

Regulation 526-01-01

Every connection between conductors and between a conductor and equipment shall provide durable electrical continuity and adequate mechanical strength (See other mechanical stresses, Regulation 522-08).

Bulkhead luminaires

Bulkhead luminaires fitted with
incandescent lamps can operate at high
temperatures.

Snag 4

A householder complained of an acrid
smell of burning. Upon investigation, it
was found that a 100 watt incandescent
lamp had been fitted in a bulkhead
luminaire with a maximum rating of
60 watts. The insulation of the fixed
wiring had degraded and the moulded
connector block had melted. The
excessive temperatures were likely to
cause a fire.

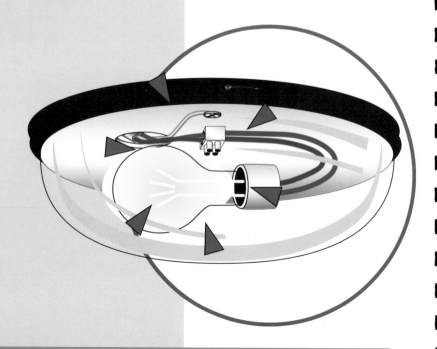

Solution

The solution to this problem is to:

- Effect repairs to the damaged equipment (the cable, the connector block and, probably, the luminaire).

- Consider selecting a replacement luminaire that can safely operate continuously with a 100 watt lamp.

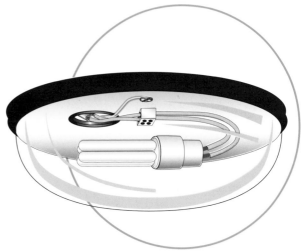

A range of solutions are available

- If this is not possible, ensure that the 100 watt lamp is replaced by a lamp with a dissipation not exceeding 60 watts.

- Consider using a Compact Fluorescent Lamp (CFL) or luminaire

- Ensure the luminaire is suitably marked and, if possible, all users of the installation made aware that, should a higher rated lamp be fitted, a risk of fire exists.

Good practice requires that, as far as possible, cables are routed away from sources of heat. Heat resisting sleeving should be installed to protect fixed installation cabling and, if necessary, the connecting cables within the luminaire. The means of connection, such as a connector block, must be suitable for the temperatures likely to be encountered. A porcelain/ceramic connector block may be required.

The use of CFLs, provided such a lamp will physically fit and is suitable for the particular mounting position, will significantly reduce the heat production, the lamp should have a longer life and consume less energy.

Heat resisting sleeving

Compact Fluorescent Lamps (CFLs).

The light output from a compact fluorescent lamp comes from phosphors that convert energy from a low pressure discharge into visible light. The colour temperature and colour rendering are determined by the phosphor mix coated on the inside of the tube. CFLs have the characteristics and advantages of linear fluorescent lamps but with compact size which is achieved by folding the discharge path while retaining high efficacy. The two main groups of CFLs are those with external control gear and those with internal control gear. High frequency control gear is now available integrated into the CFL lampholder making luminaire conversion from General Lighting Service (GLS) to CFL relatively simple. A fluorescent lamp operated at high frequency (typically at or above 30 kHz) results in a reduction of losses both in the lamp and the control gear. The control gear size and weight are less, the efficiency is higher, dimming - if required - is easier and operation is almost silent.

Regulation 522-01-01

A wiring system shall be selected and erected so as to be suitable for the highest and lowest local ambient temperature likely to be encountered.

Regulation 522-02-01 (part of)

To avoid the effects of heat from external sources including solar gain one or more of the following methods, or an equally effective method, shall be used to protect the wiring system:

(i) shielding

(ii) placing sufficiently far from the source of heat

(iii) selecting a system with due regard for the additional temperature rise which may occur

(v) local reinforcement or substitution of insulating material.

Regulation 522-02-02

Parts of a cable or flexible cord within an accessory, appliance or luminaire shall be suitable for the temperatures likely to be encountered, as determined in accordance with Regulation 522-01-01, or shall be provided with additional insulation suitable for those temperatures.

Bell wire

Bell wire, in general, is unsuitable for use in fixed installations or for connecting portable appliances.

Snag 5

The term 'bell wire' is taken to mean two-core 0.5 mm/1.036 unsheathed cable commonly-used for wiring the ELV door bell circuit of a house where an electric bell is employed.

Bell wire, often used for bell circuits or for wiring loudspeakers, is in most cases, only suitable for extra-low voltage (50 V or less).

Snags commonly-encountered centre on the use of bell wire for 230 V applications such as:

- connecting items of current-using equipment (often those having only a low consumption such as clocks and clock points)

- connecting between a ceiling rose and a lampholder

- DIY-type work (for example, a luminaire installed in a loft)

- the wiring of 230 V appliances (for example, standard lamps, table lamps or electrical tools).

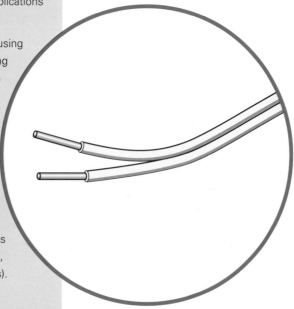

Solution

The bell wire must be replaced. A suitable replacement cable would be a pvc insulated and sheathed non-armoured cable to BS 6004. The minimum cross-sectional area of the copper conductors in a.c. power and lighting circuits must be 1 mm^2 (Regulations 524-01-01 and 524-02-01).

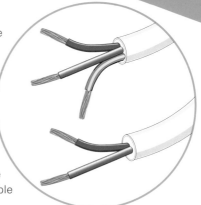

Where an appliance wired in bell flex is encountered, the reasons for the risk of danger should be explained to the user who should be encouraged to have repairs made (the cable replaced) as soon as possible.

Regulation 524-01-01 (part of)

The nominal cross-sectional area of phase conductors in a.c. circuits and of live conductors in d.c. circuits shall not be less than the values specified in Table 52C.

Type of wiring system	Use of circuit	Conductor	
		Material	Minimum permissible nominal cross-sectional area (mm^2)
Cables and insulated conductors	Power and lighting circuits	Copper Aluminium	1.0 16.0 (see Note 1)
	Signalling and control circuits	Copper	0.5 (see Note 2)
Flexible connections with insulated conductors and cables	For a specific appliance		As specified in the relevant British Standard
	For any other application	Copper	0.5 (see Note 2)
	Extra-low voltage circuits for special applications		0.5

Notes
(1)   Connectors used to terminate aluminium conductors shall be tested and approved for this specific use.
(2)   For cables containing 7 or more cores in signalling and control circuits intended for electronic equipment, a minimum nominal cross-sectional area of 0.1 mm^2 is permitted.

Regulation 524-02-01

In a single-phase circuit the neutral conductor shall have a cross-sectional area not less than the phase conductor.

Chokes in fluorescent luminaires

Chokes in fluorescent luminaires can operate at high temperatures

Snag 6

It is sometimes necessary to connect fluorescent luminaires such that cables of the fixed installation are routed past internal components in the luminaire. Internal components, such as chokes, can operate at high temperature which could result in damage to the insulation of the cable.

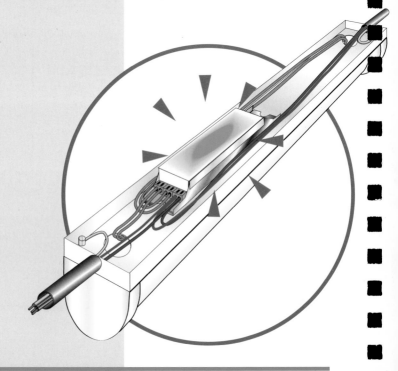

Solution

Wherever possible, the luminaire should be connected such that cables of the fixed installation do not have to travel the length of the fitting, past heat generating items such as chokes, in order to connect to the terminal block.

If this is not possible, the cables of the fixed installation should be routed away from such heat-generating components and effectively secured in place.

As an alternative, or in addition, suitable heat resisting sleeving should be employed to protect cables installed in close proximity to heat generating components.

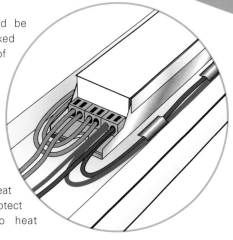

Regulation 522-01-01

A wiring system shall be selected and erected so as to be suitable for the highest and lowest local ambient temperature likely to be encountered.

Regulation 522-02-01 (part of)

To avoid the effects of heat from external sources including solar gain one or more of the following methods, or an equally effective method, shall be used to protect the wiring system:

   (i)   shielding
   (ii) placing sufficiently far from the source of heat
   (iii) selecting a system with due regard for the additional temperature rise which may occur
   (v)   local reinforcement or substitution of insulating material.

Regulation 522-02-02

Parts of a cable or flexible cord within an accessory, appliance or luminaire shall be suitable for the temperatures likely to be encountered, as determined in accordance with Regulation 522-01-01, or shall be provided with additional insulation suitable for those temperatures.

Bell circuits

A bell circuit, no less than any other circuit, must meet the requirements of BS 7671.

Snag 7

Three snags often encountered with bell circuits are:

- Bell wire is used for the bell circuit and segregation has not been provided.

- The bell circuit is not provided with proper protection against electric shock

- Short-circuit and overload conditions have not been considered.

(See snag 5)

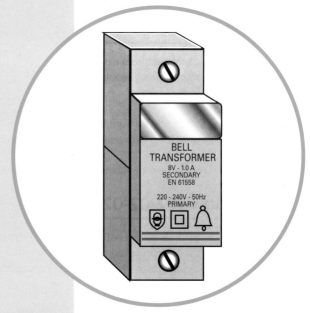

Solution

The bell circuit

The wiring of a SELV bell circuit, in most cases, must be segregated from the cables of low voltage (230V) circuits. Unsheathed cables, such as bell wire, should not be run in the same conduit, ducting, trunking as low voltage circuits, unless suitably segregated, should not be bunched with low voltage circuits, and should not be run in the same hole drilled through a joist provided for a low voltage circuit.

If it is not possible to segregate the extra-low voltage wiring, or if the safety isolating transformer is of Class I design, ordinary low voltage cable or flex should be used for the bell circuit.

Some modular consumer unit assemblies include provision for a bell transformer within the unit. When use is made of this facility, the extra-low voltage terminals and any bell wire must be effectively segregated or shrouded from low voltage parts or conductors within the enclosure. Two possible solutions to the problem are:

- use oversleeving, suitably voltage rated, on the cores of the bell wire within the distribution board
- use pvc insulated and sheathed cables (to BS 6004) for the entire secondary circuit.

Protection against electric shock

Protection against electric shock must be provided. Bell circuits are often protected by SELV according to Regulations 411-02 and 471-03 which include requirements that:

- the bell circuit must operate at extra-low voltage (normally not exceeding 50 V a.c. r.m.s or 120 V ripple-free d.c.). Bell circuits normally operate at 8 or 12 V a.c.
- the source must be suitable and will normally be a safety isolating transformer complying with BS EN 61558. The output winding must not be connected to earth
- the circuit conductors must be physically separated from those of any other system (or installed in one of four permitted ways given in Regulation 411-02-06)
- exposed-conductive-parts must not be connected to earth or earthed metalwork (Regulation 411-02-07 refers). Examples of exposed-conductive-parts in a bell circuit might include a decorative brass bell push or a metal-bodied bell.

Short-circuit and overload protection

The supply circuit to the bell transformer must be protected against overcurrent which will normally be achieved by feeding the transformer from a separate way, suitably protected, in the distribution board or consumer unit.

Bell and chime transformers to BS EN 61558 are protected against short-circuit or abnormal use in one of four ways:

- Inherently short-circuit proof. A short-circuit proof transformer is one in which the temperature under overload or short-circuit conditions and in the absence of a protective device does not exceed specified limits.

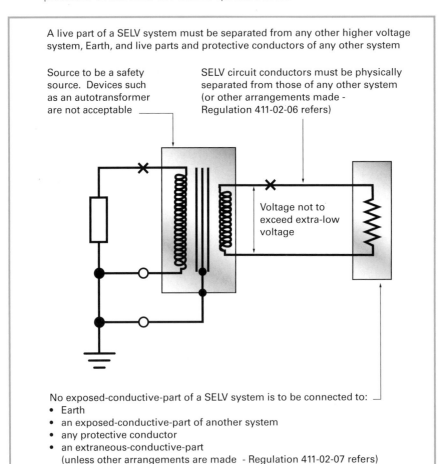

A live part of a SELV system must be separated from any other higher voltage system, Earth, and live parts and protective conductors of any other system

Source to be a safety source. Devices such as an autotransformer are not acceptable

SELV circuit conductors must be physically separated from those of any other system (or other arrangements made - Regulation 411-02-06 refers)

Voltage not to exceed extra-low voltage

No exposed-conductive-part of a SELV system is to be connected to:
- Earth
- an exposed-conductive-part of another system
- any protective conductor
- an extraneous-conductive-part
  (unless other arrangements are made - Regulation 411-02-07 refers)

- Non-inherently short-circuit proof. In this arrangement a short-circuit proof transformer is equipped with a protective device which opens the input or output circuit or reduces the current in the input or output circuit when the transformer is overloaded or short-circuited.

- Non-short-circuit proof. In this arrangement a transformer is designed to be protected against excessive temperature by means of a protective device which is not provided with the transformer.

- Fail safe. A transformer which after abnormal use fails to fuction but presents no danger to the user or the surroundings.

Further information is given in Topics S9-1 and S9-9 of the NICEIC Technical Manual

The secondary circuit, the bell circuit, must be protected against overcurrent unless the possible overcurrent is limited by the characteristics of the transformer (Regulation 431-01-01 refers). It will normally be the case for such a circuit that the conductors of the bell circuit can be considered to be protected against overcurrent because their current-carrying capacity is greater than the current that can be supplied by the transformer (Regulation 436-01-01 refers).

Regulation 411-01-01 (part of)

For protection against both direct and indirect contact, one of the following basic protective measures shall be used

i) protection by SELV according to Regulations 411-02 and 471-02.

Regulation 431-01-01

Except where the overcurrent is limited in accordance with Section 436, every live conductor shall be protected by one or more devices for automatic interruption of the supply in the event of overload current (Section 433) and fault current (Section 434), in accordance with Section 473.

Regulation 436-01-01

A conductor shall be considered to be protected against overcurrent where its current-carrying capacity is greater than the current which can be supplied by the source.

Proximity of socket-outlets to sinks

No minimum separation distance is specified where a socket-outlet is installed next to a sink but account must be taken of external influences.

Snag 8

How close can a socket-outlet or other accessory be installed to a domestic or commercial kitchen sink, or to a wash basin in a bedroom or cloakroom?

The penetration of water into an accessory could have serious effects. Water entering the terminals and mechanism may lead to corrosion, internal arcing, general degradation and eventually malfunction. Additionally, and more seriously, water may provide a track for the phase voltage to be transmitted to the front cover of the accessory, giving rise to the risk of electric shock.

Solution

The simple answer is that BS 7671 does not specify a minimum distance, however, due account has to be taken of external influences. The NICEIC recommendation is that a distance of at least 300 mm should be provided from the edge of the sink or draining board to an electrical accessory such as a switch or socket-outlet.

Domestic kitchens, bedrooms and cloakrooms (unlike bathrooms and shower rooms) are not included amongst the special installations or locations in Part 6 of BS 7671 and are not rooms where the resistance of the body is likely to be significantly reduced. Therefore, normal precautions against electric shock should be adequate and the general rules of BS 7671 are applicable.

However, whilst BS 7671 does not forbid the installation of a socket-outlet or other accessory close to a sink in a domestic kitchen, bedroom or cloakroom, the requirements of Regulation 512-06-01 have to be taken into account which means that ordinary BS 1363 socket-outlets and similar accessories are not suitable to be installed so close to sinks or draining boards that they are likely to be splashed with water or operated with wet hands.

A rule of thumb recommendation for domestic premises, to avoid the effects of splashing, is that ordinary BS 1363 socket-outlets and similar accessories should ideally be mounted not less than about 300 mm (ideally not less than about 1000 mm), in the horizontal plane, from the extremity of a sink top or wash basin.

Where splashing of accessories cannot be avoided, equipment having a degree of protection of at least IPX4 (protection against water splashing from any direction) or IPX5 (protection against water jets from any direction) is likely to be required. This type of equipment is, of course, unlikely to be visually acceptable in most domestic situations indoors.

Regulation 512-06-01

Every item of equipment shall be of a design appropriate to the situation in which it is to be used or its mode of installation shall take account of the conditions likely to be encountered, including the test requirements of Part 7.

If the equipment does not, by its construction, have the characteristics relevant to the external influences of its location, it shall be provided with appropriate additional protection in the erection of the installation. Such protection shall not adversely affect the operation of the equipment thus protected.

Two-way switching using the cpc

Circuit protective conductors of flat twin and earth cables should not be used for any other purposes.

Snag 9

A potentially dangerous snag is the use of the circuit protective conductor of a flat twin and earth cable as a live conductor in a two-way switching circuit. Danger may arise because an electrician working on the installation at a future date may, reasonably, make the assumption that the centre conductor is at Earth potential.

Protection against direct contact must be provided by one or more of the basic protective measures such as insulation of live parts or protection by a barrier or an enclosure. Regulations 412-01-01 and 412-02-01 refer. In the case of a cable, a live conductor must be completely covered by insulation. The centre conductor of a twin and earth flat sheathed cable is not covered in insulation, it is merely sheathed.

Furthermore, if the centre conductor of a flat twin and earth cable is used as a live conductor, then, probably, no circuit protective conductor will have been run to and terminated at each point in wiring and at each accessory (Regulation 471-08-08 refers).

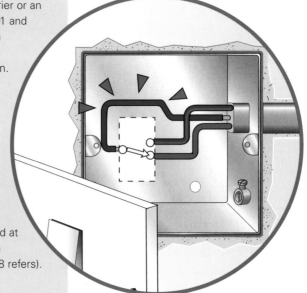

Solution

Cable incorporating three cores, colour coded brown, black and grey, plus a circuit protective conductor, represents one available option for such circuits. It must not be forgotten that, in this particular configuration, the black and grey cores are being used as phase conductors and should be suitably marked by means such as brown sleeving.

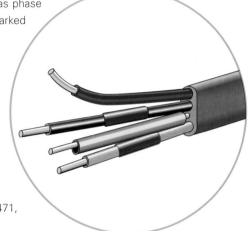

Regulation 412-01-01
(part of)

For protection against direct contact one or more of the following basic protective measures shall be used in accordance with the relevant requirements of this section and the application rules specified in Section 471, including those indicated below:

(i)   protection by insulation of live parts (Regulation 412-02 and Regulation 471-04)

(ii) protection by a barrier or an enclosure (Regulation 412-03 and Regulation 471-05).

Regulation 412-02-01 (part of)

Live parts shall be completely covered with insulation which can only be removed by destruction and which is capable of durably withstanding the electrical, mechanical, thermal and chemical stresses to which it may be subjected in service. The insulation of factory-built equipment shall comply with the relevant standards for the electrical equipment. For other equipment, protection shall be provided by insulation capable of durably withstanding the stresses to which it may be subjected in service, such as mechanical, chemical, electrical and thermal influences. Paint, varnish, lacquer, or similar products are generally not considered to provide adequate insulation for protection against direct contact in normal service.

(See snag 17 for reference to Regulation 471-08-08)

Electrical enclosures outdoors

Electrical enclosures, such as junction boxes and luminaires, located outdoors are susceptible to water entry.

Snag 10

A common defect observed in equipment located outdoors is the entry of water.

In almost all cases, water entry into electrical equipment will cause corrosion of metallic parts and water allowed to accumulate inside equipment will result in an electrical fault.

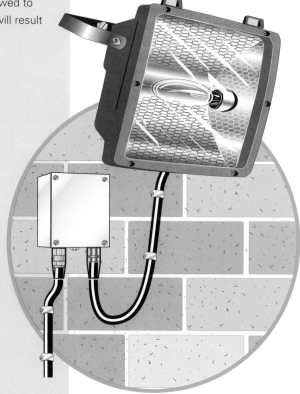

Wiring Systems

Solution

The likelihood of water penetration must be carefully assessed. The customer should be consulted upon the utilisation of equipment that might influence the assessment. The full performance details of equipment must be written into the specification or summarised on any quotation. Equipment must be specified and selected with a suitable IP (International Protection) rating to be suitable for the external influences and erected in accordance with the manufacturer's instructions. Solid foreign objects and water are both external influences, an assessment of which must be carried out for each installation (Regulation 300-01-01 refers).

Any enclosure mounted outside a building and exposed to the weather needs to be at least 'splash proof' (IPX4). This level of protection will also be required for damp conditions inside. The requirements are even more stringent in places where hoses are used, for example in dairies or pig buildings, where a minimum protection against water entry of IPX5 is required. Note that the terms 'waterproof' or 'weatherproof' should be avoided because they are not specified in the IP code.

The degrees of protection provided by an enclosure are indicated by a designation consisting of the letters 'IP' followed by two characteristic numerals and up to one additional letter and one supplementary letter, as indicated in the following diagram.

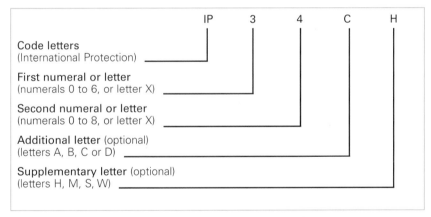

The first numeral or letter

The first numeral or letter of an IP Code designation indicates (a) the degree of protection for persons against access to hazardous parts and (b) the degree of protection of equipment within the enclosure against the ingress of solid foreign objects.

First numeral or letter*	(a)/ (b)	Brief description	Definition
0	(a)	Not protected	
	(b)	Not protected	
1	(a)	Protected against access to hazardous parts with the back of a hand	The access probe, a sphere 50 mm diameter, shall have adequate clearance from hazardous parts
	(b)	Protected against solid foreign objects of 50 mm diameter and greater	The object probe, a sphere 50 mm diameter, shall not fully penetrate[†]
2	(a)	Protected against access to hazardous parts with a finger	The jointed test finger 12 mm in diameter and 80 mm in length shall have adequate clearance from hazardous parts (see figure)
	(b)	Protected against solid foreign objects of 12.5 mm diameter and greater	The object probe, a sphere 12.5 mm diameter, shall not fully penetrate[†]
3	(a)	Protected against access to hazardous parts with a tool	The access probe of 2.5 mm in diameter shall not penetrate
	(b)	Protected against solid foreign objects of 2.5 mm diameter and greater	The access probe of 2.5 mm in diameter shall not penetrate at all[†]
4	(a)	Protected against access to hazardous parts with a wire	The access probe of 1.0 mm in diameter shall not penetrate
	(b)	Protected against solid foreign objects of 1.0 mm diameter and greater	The object probe of 1.0 mm in diameter shall not penetrate at all[†]

First numeral or letter*	(a)/(b)	Brief description	Definition
5	(a)	Protected against access to hazardous parts with a wire	The access probe of 1.0 mm in diameter shall not penetrate
	(b)	Dust-protected	Ingress of dust is not totally prevented, but dust shall not penetrate in a quantity sufficient to interfere with satisfactory operation of the apparatus or to impair safety
6	(a)	Protected against access to hazardous parts with a wire	The access probe of 1.0 mm in diameter shall not penetrate
	(b)	Dust-tight	No ingress of dust

* Where the first characteristic numeral is not required to be specified, it is replaced by the letter 'X'

† The full diameter of the object probe shall not pass through the opening of the enclosure.

Generally, an enclosure providing a specified degree of protection indicated by the first characteristic numeral also provides all lower degrees of protection indicated by that numeral. For example, where the first characteristic numeral is 3, the enclosure also provides degrees of protection of 2, 1 and 0 indicated by that numeral.

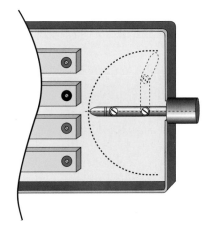

Use of the jointed test finger to establish that an enclosure protects persons against access to hazardous parts.

The second numeral or letter

The second numeral or letter denotes protection against the ingress of water given by the IP Code, as summarized in the Table below. The assessment of the extent to which an enclosure will be exposed to water should identify the most onerous conditions likely to occur.

Second numeral	Brief description
0	Not protected
1	Protected against vertically falling water drops
2	Protected against vertically falling drops when the enclosure is tilted at any angle up to 15 degrees
3	Protected against spraying water
4	Protected against splashing water
5	Protected against water jets
6	Protected against powerful water jets
7	Protected against the effects of temporary immersion in water
8	Protected against the effects of continuous immersion in water

Generally, an enclosure having a specified degree of protection indicated by the second numeral also provides all lesser degrees of protection. For example, where the second characteristic numeral is 4, the enclosure also provides degrees of protection of 3, 2, 1 and 0. However, where the second characteristic numeral is 7 or 8, the enclosure should, in the absence of better information, be considered unsuitable for exposure to water jets (designated by a second characteristic numeral of 5 or 6).

It is important to note that, in some of the locations of increased electric shock risk covered by Chapter 6 of BS 7671 (Special installations and locations), minimum degrees of protection against external influences are specified for electrical equipment enclosures. For example, in an installation at agricultural or horticultural premises, enclosures must provide protection to at least IP 44. Higher degrees of protection may be required as appropriate to the external influences (Regulation 605-11-01 refers).

Water may be permitted to enter an enclosure provided it is not in such quantity to cause damage to the enclosed equipment. It is therefore permissible to have suitably located drainage points in, say, an IPX3 enclosure in a wiring system where water may collect or condensation may form to permit its harmless escape (Regulation 522-03-02).

Additional letters

These are optional and they indicate the degree of protection of persons against access to hazardous parts. Additional letters are used where:

- the actual protection against access to hazardous parts is greater than that indicated by the first numeral or letter (for example, where greater protection is provided by barriers, suitable shape of openings or distances inside the enclosure), or

- only protection against access to hazardous parts is indicated, the first characteristic numeral then being replaced by the letter 'X'.

The Table gives the meaning of each additional letter.

Additional letter	Brief description	Definition
A	Protected against access with the back of the hand	The access probe, a sphere of 50 mm diameter, is required to have adequate clearance from hazardous parts
B	Protected against access with a finger	The jointed test finger of 12 mm diameter and 80 mm length is required to have adequate clearance from hazardous parts
C	Protected against access with a tool	The access probe of 2.5 mm diameter and 100 mm in length is required to have adequate clearance from hazardous parts
D	Protected against access with a wire	The access probe of 1.0 mm diameter and 100 mm in length is required to have adequate clearance from hazardous parts

Supplementary letters

The Table gives the most commonly used supplementary letters but further letters may be introduced by future product specifications.

Supplementary letter	Significance
H	High-voltage apparatus
M	Tested for harmful effects due to the ingress of water when the movable parts of the equipment (e.g. the rotor of a rotating machine) are in motion
S	Tested for harmful effects due to the ingress of water when the movable parts of the equipment (e.g. the rotor of a rotating machine) are stationary
W*	Suitable for use under specified weather conditions and provided with additional protective features and processes

*. In the first edition of international standard IEC 529 the letter 'W' with the same meaning was placed immediately after the code letters 'IP'.

Where more than one supplementary letter is to be used, such letters should appear in alphabetical order.

In summary

Equipment and wiring systems outdoors should be erected and located to minimize the possibility of water entry. For example, enclosures may be able to be sited under cover. Cables should, normally, be arranged to enter an enclosure from below and a sealing washer may need to be fitted to ensure the required IP rating is achieved. The manufacturer's instructions should provide further details.

Regulation 300-01-01 (part of)

An assessment shall be made of the following characteristics of the installation in accordance with the chapters indicated

(ii) the external influences to which it is to be exposed (Chapter 32)

Regulation 512-06-01

Every item of equipment shall be of a design appropriate to the situation in which it is to be used or its mode of installation shall take account of the conditions likely to be encountered, including the test requirements of Part 7.

If the equipment does not, by its construction, have the characteristics relevant to the external influences of its location, it shall be provided with appropriate additional protection in the erection of the installation. Such protection shall not adversely affect the operation of the equipment thus protected.

Regulation 522-03-01

A wiring system shall be selected and erected so that no damage is caused by condensation or ingress of water during installation, use and maintenance.

Regulation 522-03-02

Where water may collect or condensation may form in a wiring system provision shall be made for its harmless escape through suitably located drainage points.

Direct burying of cables

Armoured or metal sheathed cables may be buried in the ground but suitable precautions must be taken.

Snag 11

It is not permitted to simply bury a length of pvc/pvc twin and earth cable for purposes such as providing power to a garage, outbuilding or external lights.

In the event that an unprotected buried cable is penetrated by the sharp point of a tool, such as a spade, injury may result from the explosive effects of arcing current and by any associated fire or flames which may result. Such effects can also result when a cable is crushed severely enough to cause internal contact between the conductors or between the metallic sheathing and one or more conductors. A cable can be physically damaged by people walking on it, wheelbarrows, vehicles, and sharp stones.

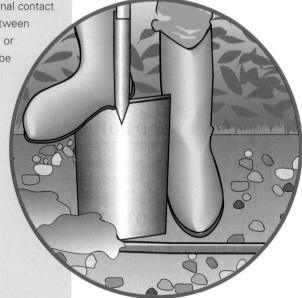

Solution

Earthed armour or metal sheath or both

A cable that will be buried directly in the ground will, in many instances, be a steel wire armoured (swa) cable complying with an appropriate British Standard. The armour or sheath is required to be suitable for use as a protective conductor, and to be earthed. As an alternative, equivalent protection for an unarmoured cable can be provided by a suitable conduit or duct.

Buried conduits and ducts

A suitable conduit or duct for an underground unarmoured cable may consist of a pipe made of earthenware, steel, concrete, polypropylene or similar material giving adequate mechanical protection or, for larger installations, a brick-built duct with a concrete slab roof.

Buried cables to be marked

The purpose of marking buried cables is to warn persons excavating the ground of the presence of a cable. Buried cables should normally be marked by tiles or covers or suitable marking tape. Tape should be yellow with a blue legend. Cable tiles can provide protection for cables when excavation work is being performed. Conduits and ducts are also to be identified by one of these methods (Regulation 522-06-03 refers). Additional cables markers are sometimes used above ground to indicate the route of an underground cable for the purpose of establishing record drawings.

Sufficient depth

Underground low voltage cables must be laid deep enough (normally taken as a minimum of 600 mm, in the absence of more precise requirements) so that they are unlikely to sustain damage from the use of hand tools such as spades, forks and picks (unless being used for excavation work). The present and potential use of the ground should be taken into consideration. For example, if the ground is to be subsequently landscaped, it may be prudent to lay the cable at a greater depth.

Further guidance may be found in HSE guidance booklet HS(G)47, which suggests that underground cables should be laid in trenches normally between 450 mm and 1 m in depth, depending on the specific site details. If there is a particular need to do so, and suitable measures are taken to provide additional mechanical protection, cables could be laid at a depth of less than 450 mm. This may be applicable where, for example, a cable is run below a concrete path or similar structure. However, the reduced depth of cover should be clearly indicated on the 'as-installed' record drawings.

Conversely, it may be prudent to increase the buried depth to at least 1 m where roads are crossed, and to lay the cable in a conduit or duct for ease of access in the future. As these depths must exist after final levelling of the ground, the initial depths may well have to be greater in order to allow for landscaping, settlement or other changes.

Digging the trench and burying the cable

Excavated surface materials should be stacked separately from sub-soils so that correct compaction and reinstatement can be obtained when back-filling. Moreover, all the excavated material should be cleared from the edge of the trench so that `rolling back' does not occur.

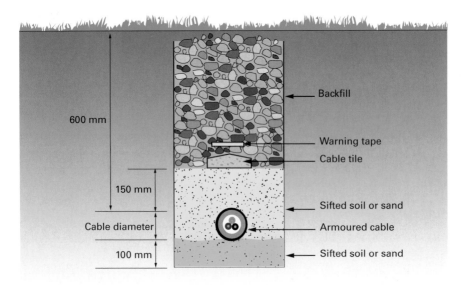

600 mm

150 mm

Cable diameter

100 mm

Backfill

Warning tape

Cable tile

Sifted soil or sand

Armoured cable

Sifted soil or sand

The bottom of the trench should be free from stone and bedded with riddled earth or sand before the cable is laid in the trench.

Prior to back-filling, a visual inspection of the following points should be made:

- ✓ The cable has a satisfactory bedding
- ✓ The spacing is correct where there is more than one cable in the trench
- ✓ The cables, where it emerges from the trench, is suitably protected
- ✓ The cable is free from obvious damage caused by installation.

When back-filling the cables should first be surrounded and covered with sand or riddled soil as necessary to give a compacted cover of at least 50 mm thickness.

Only then should the tiles or plastic marker tape be placed centrally over the cables. The tiles or tape should be laid such that future excavation work will expose it at approximately 300 to 500 mm depth.

DANGER ELECTRIC CABLE 800 mm FROM WALL

The next layer of back-fill should be placed manually and compacted by hand until a thickness of 150 mm over the tiles or marking tape has been reached. The remaining backfilling and compacting can be undertaken using mechanical equipment but consolidation should be obtained by compaction in layers of no greater than 150 mm thickness.

Regulation 522-06-03

Except where installed in a conduit or duct which provides equivalent protection against mechanical damage, a cable buried in the ground shall incorporate an earthed armour or metal sheath or both, suitable for use as a protective conductor, or be of insulated concentric construction. Buried cables shall be marked by cable covers or a suitable marking tape. Buried conduits and ducts shall be suitably identified. Buried cables, conduits and ducts shall be at a sufficient depth to avoid being damaged by any reasonably foreseeable disturbance of the ground.

Strain at glands of armoured cables

A cable must be properly fixed and supported throughout its length. In most cases, an armoured cable gland should not be used as a means of support.

Snag 12

Failure to adequately support an armoured cable can produce a considerable strain at the made-off end with consequences including:

The gland plate is subjected to undue stress and becomes distorted. The situation can become worse if two or more unsupported armoured cables are terminated on to a single gland plate.

The enclosure can become distorted or damaged.

Some or all of the steel wires of the armouring may become disengaged from the gland, producing a degradation of the earthing arrangements and a reduction in mechanical strength. Under adverse conditions the armouring can be pulled out of the gland putting strain on the conductor terminations and leaving the armour unearthed.

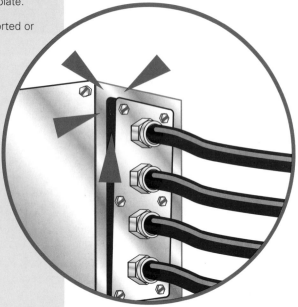

Solution

A cable gland must not be subject to undue strain either due to the unsupported weight of the cable or due to a bend in the cable in the vicinity of the gland placing undue lateral strain on the gland (Regulations 522-08-04 and 522-08-05 refer).

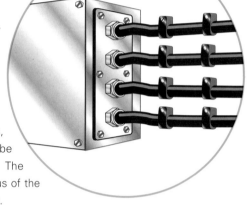

A gland is a means of properly making-off a cable and is, in most cases, not intended to be a means of support. It should be ensured that cable glands are not subjected to any significant strain. The cable must be properly supported throughout its length. Cleats, saddle supports, ties, etc must be properly selected and installed. The recommended minimum bending radius of the cable must be observed (See Snag 14).

Regulation 522-08-04

Where a conductor or a cable is not continuously supported it shall be supported by suitable means at appropriate intervals in such a manner that the conductor or cable does not suffer damage by its own weight.

Regulation 522-08-05

Every cable or conductor used as fixed wiring shall be supported in such a way that it is not exposed to undue mechanical strain and so that there is no appreciable mechanical strain on the terminations of the conductors, account being taken of mechanical strain imposed by the supported weight of the cable or conductor itself.

Unexpected joint box

An 'unexpected' joint box should be avoided, wherever possible.

Snag 13

It is not acceptable to make a connection in a cable using a joint box with screw terminals and then plaster over. Screw connections must be accessible for inspection, testing and maintenance since a loose connection may result in a risk of arcing or overheating.

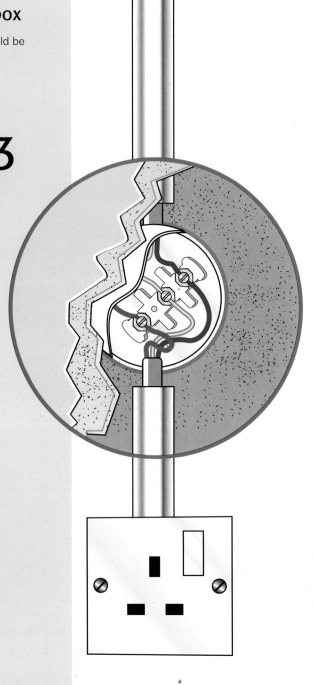

Solution

A joint box is sometimes installed because the cable, after being pulled in, is found to be too short or has been damaged or the planned location of an accessory is unsuitable[†].

If a cable is too short or is damaged it should be replaced by a cable which is longer and if an accessory has to be relocated, the supply cable should also be relocated. However, where such solutions are impracticable, there is no regulatory reason why a joint box could not form part of the circuit, providing the applicable requirements are met.

The connections within the joint box, if made by screws, must be accessible (Regulation 526-04-01 refers). Furthermore, the joint box should be properly supported, as should the cables, so that there is no strain on the connections.

[†]Note that should an accessory be relocated the requirements of Regulation 522-06-06 concerning cables in safe zones must still be met.

Regulation 526-04-01

Except for the following, every connection and joint shall be accessible for inspection, testing and maintenance:

(i) a compound-filled or encapsulated joint

(ii) a connection between a cold tail and a heating element (e.g. a ceiling and floor heating system, a pipe trace-heating system)

(iii) a joint made by welding, soldering, brazing or compression tool

(iv) a joint forming part of the equipment complying with the appropriate product standard.

Bending radii of cables

A cable may be damaged by being bent to a radius smaller than a given value.

Snag 14

During installation, cables are often dressed or bent to go around the corner of a wall, along a contour of a roof or through holes in walls or timber joists. Care must be taken not to bend a cable to a radius smaller than the recommended minimum value, based on its overall diameter. Otherwise damage may be caused to the conductors, insulation, sheath, armouring or serving (if any) of the cable during erection of the installation or at some other time, such as under fault conditions.

A cable should not be bent when at such a low temperature that damage might be caused to its insulation, sheath or serving, if any.

A wiring system must not be such that the bending radii of the cables within the wiring system will be less than the recommended minimum value.

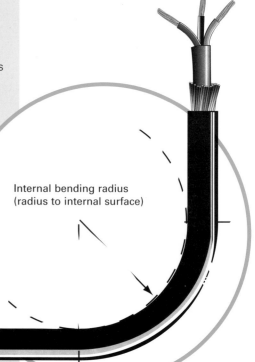

Internal bending radius (radius to internal surface)

Solution

A cable must not be bent to a radius smaller than a given value, based on its overall diameter (Regulation 522-08-03).

Table 1

Cable type	Conductor material and construction	Cable overall diameter[a]	Multiplication factor to be applied to overall diameter of cable to determine minimum internal radius of bend	
			Single-strand conductor (solid)	Multi-strand conductor
Non-armoured				
Thermoplastic (pvc) or thermosetting (XLPE or rubber)	Copper and aluminium circular and circular stranded conductors	Not exceeding 10 mm	3	2
		Exceeding 10 mm but not exceeding 25 mm	4	3
		Exceeding 25 mm	6	6
	Copper shaped conductors and solid aluminium conductors	All	8	8
Armoured				
Thermoplastic (pvc) or thermosetting (XLPE or rubber)	Copper and aluminium circular and circular stranded conductors	All	6	
	Copper shaped conductors and solid aluminium conductors	All	8	
Mineral insulated copper sheathed (MICS)				
Bare or with overall covering	Copper	All	6[b]	

a. For flat type cables the diameter refers to the major axis.

b. For MICS cables the minimum internal bending radius should normally be limited to six times the diameter of the bare copper sheath, as this will allow further straightening and reworking if necessary. However, a cable may be bent to a minimum internal bending radius of three times the diameter of the bare copper sheath, provided the bend is not re-worked.

The factors quoted in the Table comply with British Standards or, where no such information is given in the British Standard for the cable concerned, represent accepted practice. The minimum radius dimension calculated from the Table relates to the surface of the cable on the inside of the bend and can be calculated in terms of the overall diameter of the cable.

As an example of the use of the Table, consider an armoured thermosetting insulated cable having copper circular conductors and an overall diameter of 32 mm. From the Table, it can be seen that the recommended minimum internal bending radius for the cable is six times its overall diameter (i.e. 6 x 32 mm = 192 mm). Had the conductors of the cable been of the copper shaped type, the minimum recommended internal bending radius would have been eight times the overall diameter of the cable.

For a flat type cable, such as a 'twin and earth' pvc/pvc cable to BS 6004, the minimum internal bending radius is based on the major axis of the cable (rather than on the overall diameter - note 'a' beneath the Table refers).

Bending cables to the recommended minimum bending radii in the Table should be regarded as the exception rather than the rule. The bending radius should always be greater than the value given in the Table and, in practice, the greatest that circumstances will permit.

Low temperatures

A cable should not be bent when at such a low temperature that damage might be caused to its insulation, sheath or serving, if any. British Standards for cables recommend that for a cable having a standard thermoplastic (pvc) sheath, installation (including bending) should take place only when both cable and ambient temperature are above 0°C and have been so for the previous 24 hours, or when special precautions have been taken to maintain the cable at above this temperature.

Bends in wiring systems

The radius of every bend in a conduit, trunking or
ducting must be such that the bending radii of the
cables inside will not be less than the recommended minimum given in the Table.

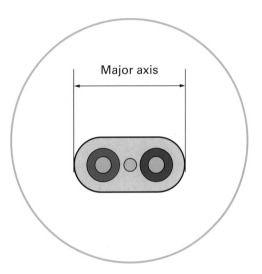

Major axis

Regulation 522-08-03

The radius of every bend in a wiring system shall be such that conductors and cable
shall not suffer damage.

Enclosure of cores of sheathed cables

The cores of a cable from which the sheath has been removed must be properly enclosed.

Snag 15

Instances are often found of exposed cable cores, as shown in the diagram, resulting from the removal of an excessive amount of the sheath of the cable. The cable cores are exposed meaning there is an increased risk of electric shock.

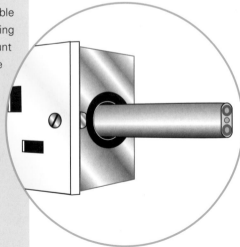

Solution

Care must be taken when removing the sheath of a cable to expose the cores in that a sufficient, but not excessive amount, of the sheath should be removed. A cable, such as a pvc/pvc insulated and sheathed cable, when properly installed provides protection against electric shock (Regulation 471-09-04 refers). In most cases, such as the example shown, the sheath of the cable must enter the accessory (Regulation 526-03-03 refers). Cable sheaths must be protected from any sharp edges at the enclosure by deburring or providing a suitable grommet. Enclosures must, in almost every case, provide at least a degree of protection of IP2X or IPXXB (which prevents the entry of solid objects exceeding 12.5 mm diameter, for example, a finger or tools.

Definition:

Enclosure: *A part providing protection of equipment against certain external influences and in any direction protection against direct contact.*

Regulation 471-09-04

Cable having a non-metallic sheath or a non-metallic enclosure shall not be described as being of Class II construction. However, the use of such cable installed in accordance with Chapter 52 shall be deemed to afford satisfactory protection against direct and indirect contact.

Regulation 526-03-03

Cores of sheathed cables from which the sheath has been removed and non-sheathed cables at the termination of conduit, ducting or trunking shall be enclosed as required by Regulation 526-03-02

Regulation 526-03-02

Every termination and joint in a live conductor or a PEN conductor shall be made within one of the following or a combination thereof:

(i) a suitable accessory complying with the appropriate British Standard

(ii) an equipment enclosure complying with the appropriate British Standard

(iii) a suitable enclosure of material complying with the glow-wire test requirements of BS 6458-2.1

(iv) an enclosure formed or completed with building material considered to be non-combustible when tested to BS 476-4

(iv) an enclosure formed or completed by part of the building structure, having the ignitability characteristic 'P' as specified in BS 476 Part 5.

Supply to a smoke alarm

BS 5839-6 (1995)* gives recommendations for the supply to a main-powered smoke alarm in a dwelling

Snag 16

Is it permitted to supply a smoke alarm in a dwelling from a local lighting circuit?

* Note that BS 5839-6 is under revision (2004).

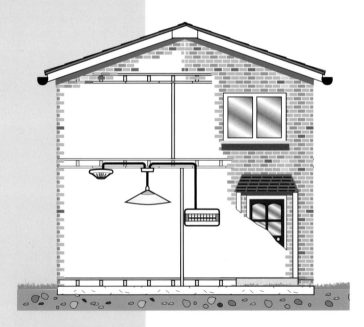

Grade D system

Solution

Mains powered smoke alarms forming part of a fire detection and alarm system in a dwelling should be supplied from:

- an independent circuit or a separately electrically protected regularly used local lighting circuit (Grade D systems), or

- an independent circuit (Grade E systems).

Grade D system

A smoke alarm for a Grade D system can be supplied either from a separate, regularly-used lighting circuit or from an independent circuit at the dwelling's main distribution board.

If more than one smoke alarm is to be installed, all smoke alarms should be connected on a single final circuit and the smoke alarms should be of a type that may be interconnected. *(See snag 19)*

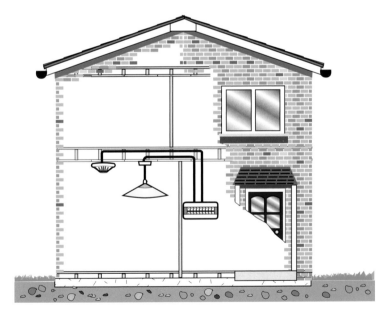

Grade E system

Grade E system

A smoke alarm for a Grade E system should be supplied from an independent circuit at the dwelling's main distribution board and no other equipment can be supplied by the circuit (except for a monitoring device - see BS 5839-6 for details*).

The dedicated circuit supplying a Grade E system should, preferably, not have RCD protection. However, if RCD protection is necessary for reasons of electrical safety (for example in a TT installation) then either:

- The RCD should only serve the circuit supplying the smoke alarms, or

- The RCD protection of the fire alarm circuit should operate independently of any RCD protection for circuits supplying socket-outlets or portable equipment.

Grades of system

The Grades of fire alarm system extend from A to F. The definitions of Grade D, E and F systems (from BS 5839 Part 6*) are as follows:

Grade D	A system of one or more mains-powered smoke alarms, each with an integral standby supply
Grade E	A system of one or more mains-powered smoke alarms with no standby supply
Grade F	A system of one or more battery-powered smoke alarms.

The Grade of system relates to the engineering aspects of the fire detection and fire alarm system and higher grades of system tend to provide a greater level of control and monitoring of the system or greater reliability and availability to perform correctly in the event of a fire. The grade of system that needs to be installed depends on the nature of the dwelling, the level of the fire risk and the characteristics of the occupants. The Grade of system may be the subject of legislative control or requirements placed by the insurer.

For new dwellings, a Grade E system or higher is, in most cases, acceptable. Reference should be made to BS 5839-6 (1995) Table 2*.

A smoke alarm, as with any fire detection and alarm system, installed in a dwelling has to meet:

- The recommendations of BS 5839: *Fire detection and fire alarm systems for buildings*: Part 6: *Code of practice for the design, installation and maintenance of fire detection and fire alarm systems in dwellings* (under revision) and

- The electrical safety requirements of BS 7671: *Requirements for Electrical Installations* and

- Part B Fire safety of the Building Regulations 1991 (2000 Edition).

* Note that BS 5839-6 is under revision (2004).

Cables at a junction box

Circuit protective conductors should not be terminated outside a junction box.

Snag 17

Circuit protective conductors (cpcs) are not always terminated properly at accessories. Instances have been observed of protective conductors being terminated outside a junction box, as illustrated.

The snag with this method of termination is that the protective conductors are more likely to suffer damage due to being unenclosed and unprotected. A damaged cpc or connection could result in failure of the circuit to disconnect under earth fault conditions leading to a risk of electric shock or fire.

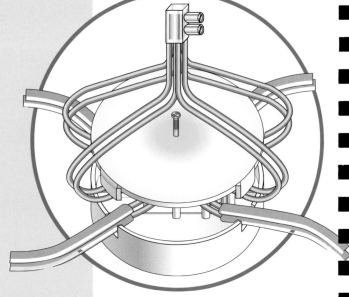

Solution

In the example shown where eight cables are to be terminated; one solution would be to employ two junction boxes.

The cores of sheathed cables must be enclosed. Regulations 526-03-02 and 526-03-03 refer. Regulation 526-03-03 deals with the enclosure of the cores of cables from which the sheath has been removed and Regulation 526-03-02 gives details of the permitted types of enclosure. All the conductors of the cable must be taken into the junction box and terminated. The protective conductor must be terminated at each accessory as required by Regulation 471-08-08.

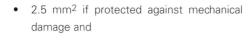

A copper protective conductor of cross-sectional area less than:

- 2.5 mm² if protected against mechanical damage and

- 4 mm² if not protected against mechanical damage

must be contained within an enclosure formed by a wiring system (Regulation 543-01-01 refers).

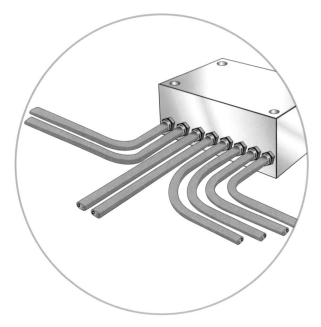

Regulation 471-08-08

In every installation which provides for protection against indirect contact by automatic disconnection of supply, a circuit protective conductor shall be run to and terminated at each point in wiring and at each accessory except a lampholder having no exposed-conductive-parts and suspended from such a point.

Regulation 526-03-03

Cores of sheathed cables from which the sheath has been removed and non-sheathed cables at the termination of conduit, ducting or trunking shall be enclosed as required by Regulation 526-03-02.

Wiring Systems   snags and solutions © NICEIC

Regulation 526-03-02

Every termination and joint in a live conductor or a PEN conductor shall be made within one of the following or a combination thereof:

(i) a suitable accessory complying with the appropriate British Standard

(ii) an equipment enclosure complying with the appropriate British Standard

(iii) a suitable enclosure of material complying with the glow-wire test requirements of BS 6458-2.1

(iv) an enclosure formed or completed with building material considered to be non-combustible when tested to BS 476-4

(iv) an enclosure formed or completed by part of the building structure, having the ignitability characteristic 'P' as specified in BS 476 Part 5.

Regulation 543-01-01 (part of)

The cross-sectional area of every protective conductor, other than an equipotential bonding conductor, shall be:

(i) calculated in accordance with Regulation 543-01-03, or

(ii) selected in accordance with Regulation 543-01-04.

If the protective conductor:

(iii) is not an integral part of a cable, or

(iv) is not formed by conduit, ducting or trunking, or

(v) is not contained in an enclosure formed by a wiring system;

the cross-sectional area shall not be less than 2.5 mm^2 copper equivalent if protection against mechanical damage is provided, and 4 mm^2 copper equivalent if mechanical protection is not provided.

Cables in cavity walls

Thermoplastic (pvc) insulated and sheathed cables should, normally, not be installed in external cavity walls.

Snag 18

Cables such as pvc/pvc insulated and sheathed cables installed in cavity walls may

- be damaged during installation,

- be unsupported within the cavity,

- deteriorate due to being in contact with cavity wall insulation,

- overheat due to the effects of the thermal insulation

- be attacked by flora or fauna, or

- provide a passage for water to be carried to the inner leaf.

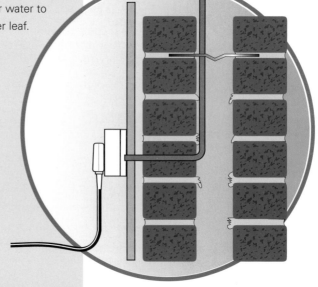

Solution

Cables should normally not be installed in external cavity walls. If it is indeed required to install a cable in a cavity wall, a sheathed mineral-insulated copper sheathed (MICS) cable may be judged by the installation designer to be suitable for such a location.

Installing pvc/pvc insulated and sheathed cables in an external cavity wall is generally an undesirable practice as it is unlikely that all of the applicable requirements of BS 7671, the Building Regulations and the NHBC requirements listed below can be met.

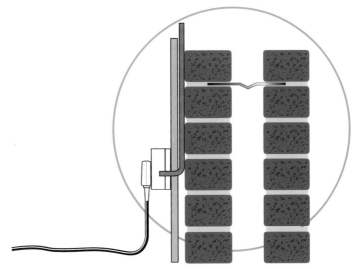

Damage to cables during installation.

Obstructions in a cavity wall, such as metal wall ties or mortar projections, create a risk of unseen damage occurring to the cable sheath and conductor insulation during installation (Regulation 522-08-01 refers).

Strain on cables lacking support

Long unsupported vertical drops may place undue strain on the conductors, leading to damage (Regulation 522-08-04 refers).

Materials liable to cause mutual or individual deterioration

Expanded polystyrene sheets, granules or foam may be used in buildings for thermal insulation purposes. If this material comes into contact with thermoplastic (pvc) cable sheathing, plasticiser can migrate from the thermoplastic to the polystyrene. The thermoplastic sheathing then becomes less flexible and the polystyrene becomes soft and tacky. Such contact should be avoided. (Regulation 522-05-03 refers).

Cables in thermal insulation

Thermal insulation is often installed in cavity walls during or after construction. Cables in the cavity may not then be able to carry the load current without overheating due to their current-carrying capacity being reduced. Cables should be installed where they will not come into contact with thermal insulation (present or reasonably to be expected in the future) unless the current-carrying capacity is adequately maintained by, for example, increasing the cross-sectional area of the conductors at the design stage. (Regulation 523-04-01 refers).

Presence of flora and fauna

Designers and installers may not necessarily detect or predict the presence of flora or fauna in a cavity wall. The wiring system should be selected to withstand all the external influences expected, or damage to cables may occur from, for example, mould or rodents. (Regulations 522-09-01 and 522-10-01 refer).

Requirements of the Building Regulations

Building Regulations 2000, Approved Document C, 1992 Edition, Section 4: Walls, paragraph 4.12 b Cavity external walls, states: 'A cavity external wall may be built with the cavity at least 50 mm wide. The cavity is to be bridged only by wall ties or by damp-proof trays provided to prevent moisture being carried to the inner leaf.' A cavity is intended to provide a gap to prevent water penetration. Cables could bridge this protection if they touch both the inner and outer leaves of a cavity wall. Furthermore, the cables could provide a route for water to drain directly into accessories, with potentially dangerous results.

NHBC Requirements

It is noteworthy that the National House-Building Council states, in Section 8.1 - S2 of NHBC Standards, that no cables other than electricity meter tails are to be located in the cavity of an external wall. Where meter tails do have to pass through the cavity, however, this does not preclude the requirements of BS 7671 referred to in this Snag having to be met.

Regulation 522-05-03

Materials liable to cause mutual or individual deterioration or hazardous degradation shall not be placed in contact with each other.

Regulation 522-08-01

A wiring system shall be selected and erected so as to minimize during installation, use and maintenance, damage to the sheath and insulation of cables and insulated conductors and their terminations.

Regulation 522-08-04

Where a conductor or a cable is not continuously supported it shall be supported by suitable means at appropriate intervals in such a manner that the conductor or cable does not suffer damage by its own weight.

Regulation 522-09-01 (flora and/or mould growth)

Where expected conditions constitute a hazard (AK2), the wiring system shall be selected accordingly or special protective measures shall be adopted.

Regulation 522-10-01 (fauna)

Where expected conditions constitute a hazard (AL2), the wiring system shall be selected accordingly or special protective measures shall be adopted.

Regulation 523-04-01 (part of)

Where a cable is to be run in a space to which thermal insulation is likely to be applied, the cable shall wherever practicable be fixed in a position such that it will not be covered by the thermal insulation. Where fixing in such a position is impracticable the cross-sectional area of the cable shall be increased appropriately.

Interconnection of Smoke alarms

Where a dwelling is fitted with more than one smoke alarm, the smoke alarms should be interconnected

Snag 19

Dwellings, increasingly, have more than one smoke alarm and, occasionally, it is found that the smoke alarms are not interconnected.

The consequences of a fire in a property may be significantly reduced by interconnecting smoke alarms thereby ensuring persons are warned of a fire at the earliest possible opportunity.

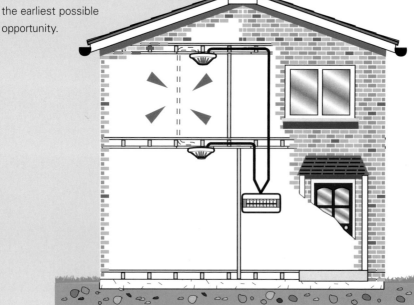

Solution

The smoke alarms should be interconnected so that both (or all) the devices will give a warning if a fire is detected.

Further information is provided in Clauses 5.6 of BS 5839: *Fire detection and alarm systems for buildings* Part 6: *Code of practice for the design and installation of fire detection and alarm systems in dwellings*, 1995 which is partly reproduced below, for convenience.

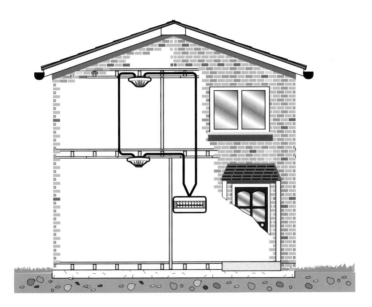

Clause 5.6 (part) System planning

If two or more smoke alarms are installed, they should normally be interconnected, whether by wiring or radio, to ensure that, when any one device detects fire, all smoke alarms in the dwelling give a fire alarm warning.

Smoke alarms in thatched properties

The significant difference between thatched properties and most other premises of similar use is the perceived, and many would conclude the real, increased risk of fire.

Snag 20

The electrical installation in a thatched property, as with any property, must be so arranged that the risk of ignition of flammable materials due to high temperature or electric arc is reduced.

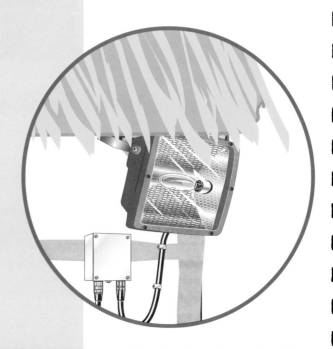

Wiring Systems

Solution

The increased risk of ignition is attributable largely to the more combustible material used for the roof. (Regulations 130-03-01 and 482-01-01 refer). However, extinguishing a fire in a thatched property is often made more difficult by virtue of the inherent quality of the thatch to repel water, including that from the firefighters' hoses. The Dorset Building Control Technical Committee gives both requirements and recommendations for thatched properties. The

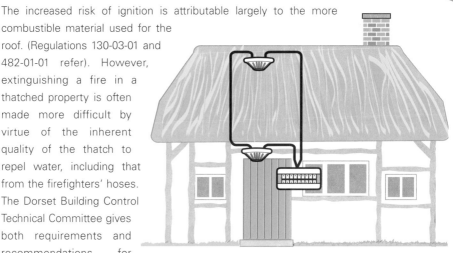

'Dorset Model' represents a uniform approach to thatched buildings which is now being advocated across Dorset where compensatory requirements are considered acceptable to achieve compliance with the Building Regulations. Requirements and recommendations extend to smoke alarm systems and electrical installations.

The Dorset Model gives recommendations concerning smoke alarms for thatched properties which are additional to those included in BS 5839: *Fire detection and alarm systems for buildings*:

- Part 6: *Code of practice for the design and installation of fire detection and alarm systems in dwellings, 1995* and

- Part 1: *Code of practice for system design, installation, commissioning and maintenance, 2002*.

A domestic mains and battery powered, interlinked smoke alarm system with one smoke alarm located in the roof void should be fitted in a thatched property. The system should generally be in accordance with that specified in BS 5839 Part 6.

In certain cases, it may be prudent to consider a smoke and fire detection and alarm system, at least within areas adjacent to the thatch, including loft(s). Fire extinguishing systems may also need to be considered, where appropriate. Furthermore:

- It is NOT recommended to cut in recessed lighting into the ceilings below the thatch.

- Light fittings within the roof space to be in a bulkhead fitting.

- External floodlights should not be located just under thatch.

Further information is provided in the Dorset Building Control Technical Committee document entitled: Thatched Buildings, 'The Dorset Model'.

www.dorset-technical-committee.org.uk

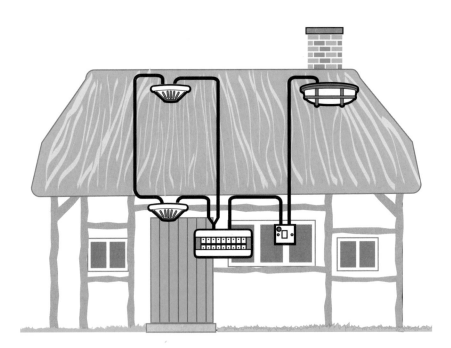

Regulation 130-03-01

So far as is reasonably practicable the electrical installation shall be so arranged that the risk of ignition of flammable materials due to high temperature or electric arc is reduced. In addition, during normal operation of the electrical equipment, the risk of burns to persons or livestock shall be reduced so far as is reasonably practicable.

Regulation 482-01-01 (part of)

The requirements of this section are additional to those in Chapter 42 and Section 527.

This section applies to:

(ii) installations in locations constructed of combustible materials.

Electrical equipment shall be selected and erected such that its temperature in normal operation, and foreseeable temperature rise in the event of a fault, is unlikely to cause a fire, taking due account of external influences. This shall be achieved by the construction of the equipment or by additional protective measures taken during erection.

Loose male conduit bushes

It can be difficult to properly tighten male conduit bushes because of awkward access

Snag 21

One of the problems regularly encountered by NICEIC Area Engineers is loose male conduit bushes, particularly inside metal boxes where it is difficult to get an open-ended, or adjustable, spanner into position to allow adequate tightening of the bush.

A loose conduit bush will almost certainly result in a poor electrical connection. In the event of an earth fault there will no longer be a sound return path for the earth fault current.

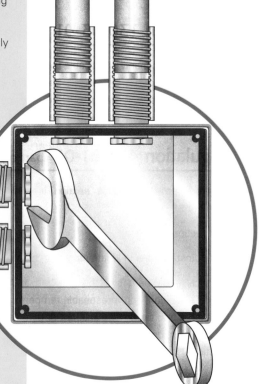

Solution

There are spanners on the market, bush spanners, which are specially designed for tightening male conduit bushes complying with BS 4568: Part 2, which specifies dimensions and tolerances for the hexagon portions of the bushes. Such spanners may, quite correctly, fit only those male bushes which fully comply with the British Standard.

Bushes may be encountered which are not marked as complying with BS 4568, possibly because the small size of the bushes means that there is insufficient space to mark them with the BS number. Some non-standard male bushes do not have sufficient width across the flats to ensure adequate electrical continuity at all times, particularly if the entry hole is oversized.

Regulation 511-01-01 states that all equipment should comply with the appropriate British or Harmonised European Standard or provide an equivalent degree of safety. Contractors are advised to specify only British Standard male bushes complying with these standards when ordering from their suppliers and should check that the correct items have been supplied.

Regulation 511-01-01

Every item of equipment shall comply with the relevant requirements of the applicable British Standard, or Harmonized Standard appropriate to the intended use of the equipment. The edition of the Standard shall be the current edition, with those amendments pertaining at a date to be agreed by the parties to the contract concerned (see Appendix 1).

Alternatively, if equipment complying with a foreign national standard based on an IEC Standard is to be used, the designer or other person responsible for specifying the installation shall verify that any differences between that standard and the corresponding British Standard or Harmonized Standard will not result in a lesser degree of safety than that afforded by compliance with the British Standard.

Condensation in conduit systems

Drainage points may be needed in steel conduit systems.

Snag 22

Internal corrosion can occur even in nominally dry situations, causing rapid deterioration and seriously affecting the function of the conduit as a protective conductor and as a means of mechanical protection.

Damp can affect steel conduit systems internally and externally and there are certain aspects of corrosion prevention which are sometimes overlooked.

Solution

To deal with this problem the Regulations require the provision of drainage points for condensed moisture in conduit systems not intended to be gas-tight (Regulations 522-03-01 and 522-03-02 refer).

Suitable drainage outlets are often provided by drilling 3 mm diameter holes at the lowest point in the underside of draw-in boxes, switch boxes, enclosed luminaires etc. Not only will this normally permit the condensation to run out of the conduit system, but it will also usually allow circulation of air within the conduit, to permit drying out.

Conduit runs most susceptible to internal condensation are those subject to rapid temperature fluctuations, but it is good practice to provide suitable ventilation for all conduit systems whatever their location except for gas-tight or flameproof installations where no ventilation is permitted.

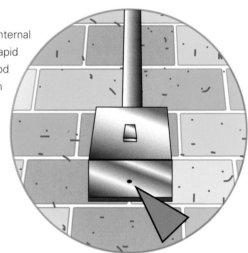

Regulation 522-03-01

A wiring system shall be selected and erected so that no damage is caused by condensation or ingress of water during installation, use and maintenance.

Regulation 522-03-02

Where water may collect or condensation may form in a wiring system provision shall be made for its harmless escape through suitably located drainage points.

Pre-galvanised threaded steel conduit

Pre-galvanized threaded steel conduit should be used with caution.

Snag 23

Pre-galvanized conduit is manufactured from galvanized steel that is welded into a tube. The welding process burns off the galvanized coating along the welded seam so that there is a band of unprotected steel along the full length of the tube, both inside and out. On occasions the unprotected steel is covered on the outside with a metallic spray - which is porous and far inferior to the galvanized remainder. Pre-galvanized conduit looks shinier and, thus, appears smarter than hot-dip galvanized conduit.

Clearly, pre-galvanized conduit does not conform to Class 4 of BS 4568: Part 1. Where the steel seam is unprotected, either inside or out, the conduit cannot even be regarded as Class 1, ie: the steel conduit does not fall within the scope of the British Standard specification. Pre-galvanized conduit should be considered only for Class 1 usage where the welded seam has been protected both inside and out, otherwise there would be a deviation from Regulations 521-04-01 and 511-01-01.

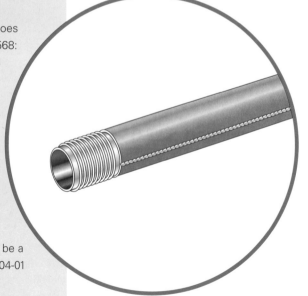

Wiring Systems

Solution

BS 4568: Part 1: 1970 is the current specification for steel conduit, bends and couplers for electrical installations. Conduit is classified according to both the method of assembly (plain or screwed) with fittings and to the type of corrosion protection applied, viz:

- Class 1 - light protection both inside and outside, eg: priming paint

- Class 2 - medium protection both inside and outside, eg: stoved (black) enamel

- Class 3 - medium/heavy protection (inside as Class 2, outside as Class 4)

- Class 4 - heavy protection both inside and outside, eg: hot-dip zinc coating (galvanized), sheradizing.

Some manufacturers have trade names for their protection processes. It may be necessary to consult the manufacturer in order to establish into which Class a specific trade-named type of protection falls.

The following tables (reproduced from BS 4568; Part 1 (as amended) gives the metric dimensions and weights for light gauge (plain) conduit and heavy gauge (screwed or plain) conduit which has a thicker wall.

Conduit, light gauge (Plain)

Nominal size	Dimensions (mm)			Weight (g/m)			
	A		B	Class 1, 2 and 3		Class 4	
	Min.	Max.		Min.	Max.	Min.	Max.
16	15.7	16.0	1.0±0.10	324	405	355	470
20	19.7	20	1.0±0.10	416	515	457	597
25	24.6	25.0	1.2±0.15	598	784	649	887
32	31.6	32.0	1.2±0.15	796	1006	861	1139

Conduit, heavy gauge (Screwed or plain)

Nominal size	Dimensions (mm)					Weight (g/m)			
	A		B	C		Class 1, 2 and 3		Class 4	
	Min.	Max.		Min.	Max.	Min.	Max.	Min.	Max.
16	15.7	16.0	1.4±0.10	11.5	13.5	452	531	483	594
20	19.7	20.0	1.6±0.15	13.0	20.0	643	783	682	862
25	24.6	25.0	1.6±0.15	16.0	18.0	811	995	860	1095
32	31.6	32.0	1.6±0.15	18.0	20.0	1069	1301	1133	1432

As shown in the tables above, dimension A is the outside diameter of the conduit, dimension B is the wall thickness and dimension C is the depth to which the end is threaded.

Conduit, light gauge (plain)   Conduit, heavy gauge (screwed or plain)

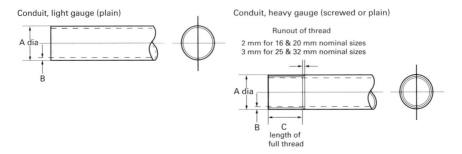

Regulation 511-01-01

Every item of equipment shall comply with the relevant requirements of the applicable British Standard, or Harmonized Standard appropriate to the intended use of the equipment. The edition of the Standard shall be the current edition, with those amendments pertaining at a date to be agreed by the parties to the contract concerned (see Appendix 1).

Alternatively, if equipment complying with a foreign national standard based on an IEC Standard is to be used, the designer or other person responsible for specifying the installation shall verify that any differences between that standard and the corresponding British Standard or Harmonized Standard will not result in a lesser degree of safety than that afforded by compliance with the British Standard.

Regulation 521-04-01

A conduit or conduit fitting shall comply with the appropriate British Standard referred to below:

(i)   steel conduit and fittings - BS 31, BS EN 60423, BS EN 50086-1

(ii) flexible steel conduit - BS 731-1, BS EN 60423, BS EN 50086-1

(iii) steel conduit fittings with metric threads - BS 4568, BS EN 60423, BS EN 50086-1

(iv) non-metallic conduits and fittings - BS 4607, BS EN 60423, BS EN 50086-2-1.

Conduit drops to motors

Conduit must be properly supported

Snag 24

A final connection to a motor in a factory or a plant room frequently presents a problem because the supply has to come from overhead and there are no walls or other structural features to provide support for the conduit drop.

Area Engineers have reported conduit drops of 5 m or more with one right-angled set and often a second, more open, set for which the only support is provided by the conduit entries at each end.

A knock from a ladder, vibration, or the use of the conduit as a hand-hold could cause damage or slackening of conduit joints leading to damage to the wiring or a high resistance connection or an open-circuit protective conductor.

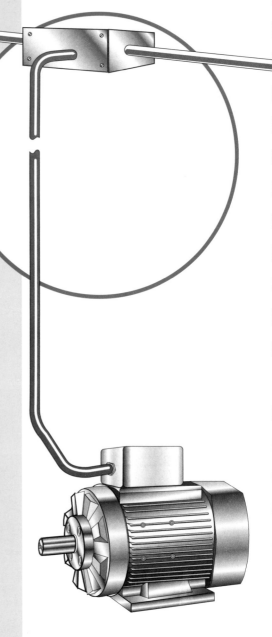

Solution

The conduit must be adequately supported, have secure fixings and be protected from mechanical damage (Regulation 522-08-01). The conduit must be protected from mechanical deterioration and electrical continuity must be assured (Regulations 543-02-05, 543-02-04 and 543-03-01 refer). Vibration of the motor must be taken account of by a means such as flexible conduit but the flexible or pliable conduit must not be used as a protective conductor (Regulation 543-02-01 refers).

Whether or not steel conduit is used as a circuit protective conductor, it is always required to provide reliable electrical continuity along its length and to be effectively and permanently connected to the Main Earthing Terminal (with certain permitted exceptions such as where SELV conductors only are installed within the conduit). Every joint in conduit must be electrically and mechanically continuous (Regulation 543-03-06 refers).

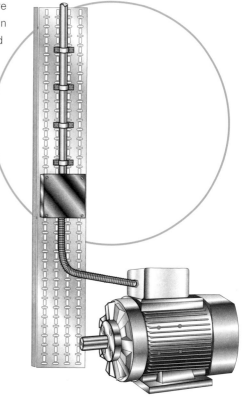

An alternative approach is to use a flexible cable or cord, preferably metal-sheathed, to supply the machine with a short length of conduit at the lower end. This conduit should be firmly fixed to the machine or a support, as shown.   The conduit should rise to about 2 m above floor level and should terminate with a ring bush or cable gland.

This method will accommodate discrepancies in the relative locations of the machine and supply point, and will provide mechanical protection adjacent to the machine.

The flexible cable or cord must be adequately supported.

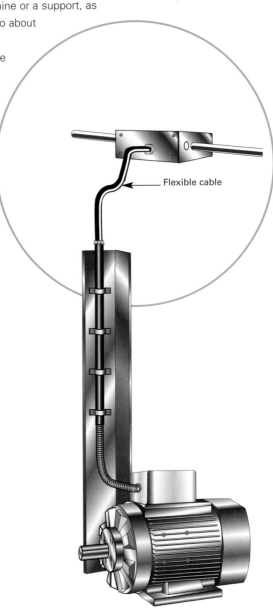

Flexible cable

Regulation 522-08-01

A wiring system shall be selected and erected so as to minimize during installation, use and maintenance, damage to the sheath and insulation of cables and insulated conductors and their terminations.

Regulation 543-02-01 (part of)

Flexible or pliable conduit shall not be selected as a protective conductor.

Regulation 543-02-05

The metal covering including the sheath (bare or insulated) of a cable, in particular the sheath of a mineral insulated cable, trunking and ducting for electrical purposes and metal conduit, may be used as a protective conductor for the associated circuit, if it satisfies both requirements of items (i) and (ii) of Regulation 543-02-04.

Regulation 543-02-04 (part of)

(i)   its electrical continuity shall be assured, either by construction or by suitable connection, in such a way as to be protected against mechanical, chemical or electrochemical deterioration, and

(ii) its cross-sectional area shall be at least equal to that resulting from the application of Regulation 543-01, or verified by test in accordance with BS EN 60439-1, and

Regulation 543-03-01

A protective conductor shall be suitably protected against mechanical and chemical deterioration and electrodynamic effects.

Regulation 543-03-06

Every joint in metallic conduit shall be mechanically and electrically continuous by screwing or by substantial mechanical clamps. Plain slip or pin-grip sockets shall not be used.

Cables installed in conduit underground

Adequate protection must be provided for cables installed underground. One option available is to employ conduit.

Snag 25

A twin-and-earth cable buried in the ground without additional mechanical protection is very likely to suffer damage and present a risk of electric shock.

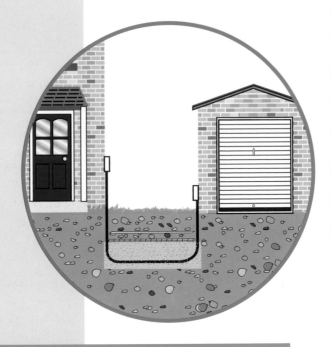

Solution

It is not permitted to simply bury a length of twin and earth cable in the ground for purposes such as providing an electrical supply to a garage, outbuilding or external luminaires.

A cable buried in the ground need not be armoured provided it is installed in a conduit which provides equivalent protection against mechanical damage. For example, suitable steel conduit may be used.

Steel conduit may be used as a protective conductor subject to compliance with Regulation 543-02-04 and 543-02-05 but must be protected against corrosion (Regulation 543-03-01 refers). Where protection against indirect contact is provided by Earthed Equipotential Bonding and Automatic Disconnection of Supply (EEBAD), the steel conduit is always required to be earthed for compliance with Regulation 413-02-06 for a TN system or 413-02-18 for a TT system.

Where steel conduit is used as a circuit protective conductor, it is always required to provide reliable electrical continuity along its length. Even if a separate protective conductor is run in steel conduit, the conduit, in most circumstances, being an exposed-conductive-part, will be required to be effectively and permanently connected to the circuit protective conductor(s) and hence to Earth. Every joint in conduit must be electrically and mechanically continuous (Regulation 543-03-06 refers).

The installation designer or installer may select non-metallic conduit or ducting. However, adequate mechanical protection for the cable must be ensured and a separate circuit protective conductor provided as appropriate.

Buried cables in conduits are to be marked by a means such as marker tape or cable tiles (Regulation 522-06-03 refers).

Further recommendations include:

- Cables installed in steel conduit underground should be sheathed.
- Steel conduit, where used underground, should be heavy gauge galvanised steel.
- A minimum buried depth of 600 mm is recommended. This depth must be achieved after final levelling of the ground and therefore the initial depth may well have to be greater to allow for landscaping or other changes.
- Additional cables markers are sometimes used above ground to indicate the route of an underground cable for purpose of establishing record drawings.

Regulation 413-02-06 (TN systems)

Each exposed-conductive-part of the installation shall be connected by a protective conductor to the main earthing terminal of the installation and that terminal shall be connected to the earthed point of the supply source in accordance with Regulations 542-01-02, 542-01-03 and 542-01-05, as appropriate.

Regulation 413-02-18 (TT systems)

Every exposed-conductive-part which is to be protected by a single protective device shall be connected, via the main earthing terminal, to a common earth electrode. However, if several protective devices are in series, the exposed-conductive-parts may be connected to separate earth electrodes corresponding to each protective device.

(Similar requirements are applicable for IT systems).

Regulation 522-06-03

Except where installed in a conduit or duct which provides equivalent protection against mechanical damage, a cable buried in the ground shall incorporate an earthed armour or metal sheath or both, suitable for use as a protective conductor, or be of insulated concentric construction. Buried cables shall be marked by cable covers or a suitable marking tape. Buried conduits and ducts shall be suitably identified. Buried cables, conduits and ducts shall be at a sufficient depth to avoid being damaged by any reasonably foreseeable disturbance of the ground.

Regulation 543-02-05

The metal covering including the sheath (bare or insulated) of a cable, in particular the sheath of a mineral insulated cable, trunking and ducting for electrical purposes, and metal conduit, may be used as a protective conductor for the associated circuit, if it satisfies both requirements of items (i) and (ii) of Regulation 543-02-04.

Regulation 543-02-04

Where a metal enclosure or frame of a low voltage switchgear or controlgear assembly or busbar trunking system is used as a protective conductor, it shall satisfy the following three requirements:

(i) its electrical continuity shall be assured, either by construction or by suitable connection, in such a way as to be protected against mechanical, chemical or electrochemical deterioration, and

(ii) its cross-sectional area shall be at least equal to that resulting from the application of Regulation 543-01, or verified by test in accordance with BS EN 60439-1, and

(iii) it shall permit the connection of other protective conductors at every predetermined tap-off point.

Regulation 543-03-01

A protective conductor shall be suitably protected against mechanical and chemical deterioration and electrodynamic effects.

Regulation 543-03-06

Every joint in metallic conduit shall be mechanically and electrically continuous by screwing or by substantial mechanical clamps. Plain slip or pin-grip sockets shall not be used.

Cutting out of cable strands

Cable strands should not be cut out in order to engage the conductor in a terminal.

Snag 26

It is poor practice to cut strands as shown when connecting a stranded cable to a terminal, as this can lead to an intermittent connection with a risk of fire.

The cable in question may be intended to supply a distant load and since the voltage drop is the dominant factor in determining the cable csa, a larger csa than that required from current considerations alone may have been selected.

A problem can arise with switchgear where the terminals may be sized on the basis of current-carrying requirements only.

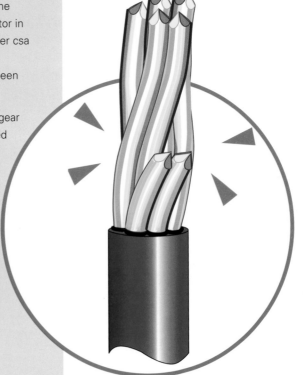

Solution

Where the csa of the conductors of the cable needs to be reduced, this must not be achieved by cutting out strands which could cause hot spots leading to premature failure of the cable. Cutting out of strands would be considered contrary to Regulation 526-01-01 relating to durable electrical continuity and adequate mechanical strength and would also contravene Regulation 526-02-01 relating to the selection of the means of connection.

A method of csa reduction that does not cause damage must be employed such as:

- Terminating the cable in an appropriate accessory and connecting to the switchgear using smaller cables, sized on current-carrying requirements, or
- Using some form of reducing 'pin lug' crimped or soldered on to the conductor
- Soldering or brazing the strands together.

Regulation 526-01-01

Every connection between conductors and between a conductor and equipment shall provide durable electrical continuity and adequate mechanical strength (See Other mechanical stresses, Regulation 522-08).

Regulation 526-02-01

The selection of the means of connection shall take account, as appropriate, of the following:

(i) the material of the conductor and its insulation

(ii) the number and shape of the wires forming the conductor

(iii) the cross-sectional area of the conductor

(iv) the number of conductors to be connected together

(v) the temperature attained by the terminals in normal service such that the effectiveness of the insulation of the conductors connected to them is not impaired

(vi) where a soldered connection is used, the design shall take account of creep, mechanical stress and temperature rise under fault current conditions

(vii) the provision of adequate locking arrangements in situations subject to vibration or thermal cycling.

Ring final circuits supplying computer equipment

Ring final circuits supplying computer equipment may have a high protective conductor current.

Snag 27

Three possible snags encountered with ring final circuits supplying computer equipment where the total protective conductor current is likely to exceed 10 mA are:

- **Accessories.** The use of socket-outlets and connection units that do not have two separate earthing terminals where the required high integrity protective connection is provided by two separate protective conductors. The risk of electric shock is increased because reliance has been placed upon a single connection.

- **Label.** Circuits having, or likely to have, a high protective conductor current not labelled at the distribution board or consumer unit. A contractor working on the circuits at a future date will be unaware that additional measures have been provided in the circuit which could result in increased risk of electric shock.

- **RCD.** A residual current device (RCD) provided to protect a circuit with high protective conductor current trips either during equipment operation or at switch-on surges.

  The problem of inconvenience caused by RCD operation can arise in a school, for example, where the local Council requires an RCD with a residual operating current not exceeding 30 mA to be incorporated in the protection of every socket-outlet circuit. As the school increases the amount of IT equipment supplied, inevitably, at some point, the RCD will trip causing inconvenience.

Solutions

See over

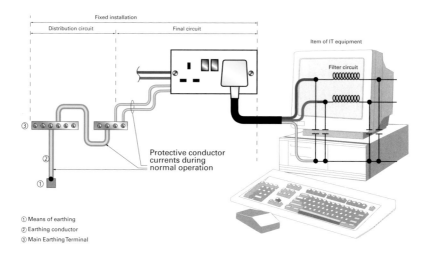

① Means of earthing
② Earthing conductor
③ Main Earthing Terminal

Solutions

When energized and in normal use, some electrical equipment causes current to flow in the circuit protective conductors. Such 'protective conductor current' (previously referred to as 'leakage current') is often associated with filters and suppressors in items such as computers. It must be ensured that the proper precautions are taken for a ring final circuit likely to have a high protective conductor current supplying socket-outlets in an installation, where, for example, it can reasonably be expected that items of IT equipment will be installed and that the protective conductor current will exceed 10 mA.

Accessories.

A ring final circuit, by its particular configuration, provides duplication of the protective conductor and, provided the requirements of Section 543 are met, a high integrity protective conductor connection exists. However, for the requirements of Section 607 to be met, the ends of each section of protective conductor in the ring must be separately terminated. Socket-outlets and accessories such as connection units must be provided with two separate earth terminals (Regulations 607-02-05 and 607-03-01 refer).

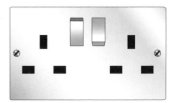

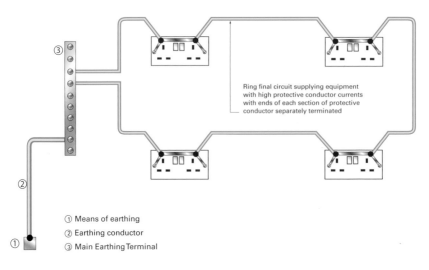

Ring final circuit supplying equipment with high protective conductor currents with ends of each section of protective conductor separately terminated

① Means of earthing
② Earthing conductor
③ Main Earthing Terminal

WARNING

High Protective Conductor Currents

The circuits identified below may have a high protective conductor current

Circuit No:

Modifications to these circuits must comply with the requirements of BS 7671: Requirements for Electrical Installations (as amended) including the supplementary requirements of Section 607: Earthing requirements for the installation of equipment having high protective conductor currents.

Label.

Where a circuit has or is likely to have a high protective conductor current, the protective conductor connection arrangements at the distribution board or consumer unit will, in many cases, be affected. For example, there will in some cases be duplicate protective conductors separately terminated. At the distribution board, information must be provided indicating those circuits having a high protective conductor current, and such information must be so positioned as to be visible to a person modifying or extending the circuit (Regulation 607-03-02 refers).

RCDs.

An RCD must be so selected and the circuits so subdivided that any protective conductor current expected to occur during normal operation of the connected load(s) will be unlikely to cause unwanted operation of the device (Regulation 531-02-04 refers).

As a rule of thumb, the designer should take care that the anticipated total protective conductor current does not exceed 25% of the rated residual operating current of the RCD. Where, for example, several items of equipment producing protective conductor current are to be supplied, it may be necessary to provide a number of separate RCD-protected circuits, each designed to supply a limited number of items appropriate to their protective conductor current. Regulation 607-07-01 refers.

In the earlier example of inconvenient RCD operation in a school; among the solutions which the installation designer should consider are:

- To provide more ring final circuits, each supplying a smaller number of socket-outlets

- To provide, with the agreement of the responsible person from the local Council, an RCD with a residual operating current not exceeding 100 mA (for example) providing the other applicable requirements of BS 7671 are met including Regulation 471-16-01 relating to socket-outlets which may reasonably be used to supply portable equipment for use outdoors

- Providing socket-outlets individually protected by an RCD (SRCDs). Such a solution would require SRCDs with two earthing terminals for the duplicated protective conductor connections and may prove expensive for larger installations.

Regulation 531-02-04

A residual current device shall be so selected and the electrical circuits so subdivided that any protective conductor current which may be expected to occur during normal operation of the connected load(s) will be unlikely to cause unnecessary tripping of the device.

Regulation 607-02-04 (part of)

The wiring of every final circuit and distribution circuit intended to supply one or more items of equipment such that the total protective conductor current is likely to exceed 10 mA, shall have a high integrity protective connection complying with one or more of the following:

(iii) two individual protective conductors each complying with the requirements of Section 543.

Regulation 607-02-05

Where two protective conductors are used in accordance with Regulation 607-02-04(iii), the ends of the protective conductors shall be terminated independently of each other at all connection points throughout the circuit, e.g. the distribution board, junction boxes and socket-outlets. This requires an accessory to be provided with two separate earth terminals.

Regulation 607-03-01 (part of)

For a final circuit with a number of socket-outlets or connection units intended to supply several items of equipment, where it is known or reasonably to be expected that the total protective conductor current in normal service will exceed 10 mA, the circuit shall be provided with a high integrity protective conductor connection complying with the requirements of Regulation 607-02 and 607-04. The following arrangements of the final circuit are acceptable:

    (i)   a ring final circuit with a ring protective conductor. Spurs, if provided, require high integrity protective conductor connection complying with the requirements of Regulation 607-02.

Regulation 607-03-02

At the distribution board information shall be provided indicating those circuits having a high protective conductor current. This information shall be positioned so as to be visible to a person who is modifying or extending the circuit.

Regulation 607-07-01

Where more than one item of equipment having a protective conductor current exceeding 3.5 mA in normal service is to be supplied from an installation incorporating a residual current device, the circuit arrangement shall be such that the residual current which may be expected to occur, including switch-on surges, will not trip the device.

Where compliance with this regulation cannot be otherwise achieved the items of equipment shall be supplied through a double-wound transformer or equivalent device as described in item (v) of Regulation 607-02-04 satisfying the requirements of that regulation.

Borrowed neutral

The wiring of each final circuit is required to be kept electrically separate from every other final circuit.

Snag 28

One of the most dangerous practices that can be perpetrated is to 'borrow' the neutral of another circuit. Contractors should be aware of the dangers to electrically-skilled operatives of such malpractice. A dangerous trap is created for any operative carrying out maintenance work or other installation alteration or extension in the future.

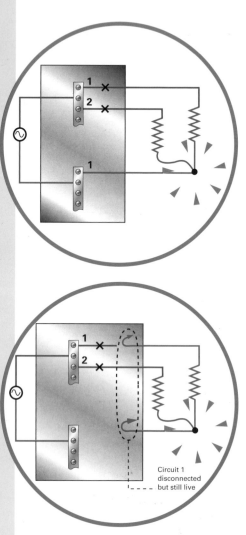

In this example of a borrowed neutral, instead of running the neutral of circuit no 2 back to the distribution board, a short cut has been taken and the neutral of circuit no 1 has been 'borrowed'.

Circuit no 1 has been disconnected; however, due to the borrowed neutral, the circuit remains energized from circuit no 2 and any person working on circuit no 1 is at risk of electric shock.

Circuit 1
disconnected
but still live

Solution

'Borrow' is a misnomer: there is no intention to disconnect (ie: 'return') the borrowed neutral. In some parts of the country the practice is referred to as 'pinching' or 'stealing' the neutral or to 'crossed neutrals' (particularly in the case of adjacent ring final circuits).

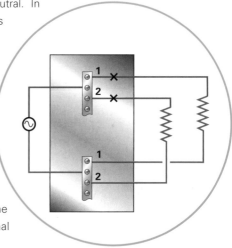

The NICEIC does, occasionally, come across cases where a neutral conductor from an upstairs lighting circuit is borrowed for a ground floor staircase luminaire or vice versa.

The neutral must be taken from the same final circuit, never from another final circuit.

This is essential not only to avoid danger during a fault but also to facilitate safe operation, inspection, testing and maintenance of the installation. The requirements are normally met by connecting each final circuit to a separate way in a distribution board.

Where an installation comprises more than one final circuit, each final circuit must be connected to a separate way in a distribution board. The wiring of each final circuit must be electrically separate from that of every other final circuit, so as to prevent the indirect energising of a final circuit intended to be isolated. Every contractor should be aware of the need to ensure that circuits are kept separate from one another. This is necessary not only to avoid danger during a fault but also to facilitate safe operation, inspection, testing and maintenance.

The neutral is, by definition, a live conductor (so that regulation 14 of the Electricity at Work Regulations is applicable) and should always be treated as live until it is isolated and **proved to be dead**. It is important that where it is necessary to disconnect the neutral, it is undertaken with insulated tools, and that the neutral conductor is not touched until proved dead.

A neutral must be never be taken from a TP&N or SP&N board to supply a circuit fed from a TP only board.

TP = Three-phase   TP&N = Three-phase and neutral

SP = Single -phase   SP&N = Single-phase and neutral

The problem of a borrowed neutral can arise with certain lighting tracks. Some luminaire manufacturers produce what is sometimes referred to as 'multi-circuit' lighting track which permits the connection of each luminaire on to the track to make contact with a choice of different lighting track conductors. In terms of live conductors, lighting tracks often have two or more phase conductors but only one neutral conductor. These lighting tracks are intended for use on a single final circuit where some luminaires are to be switched independently of others on the

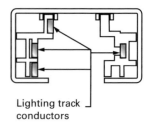

Lighting track conductors

same lighting track. Such a lighting track must never be used with more than one final circuit supplying it as this is potentially very dangerous because of the 'borrowed neutral' scenario.

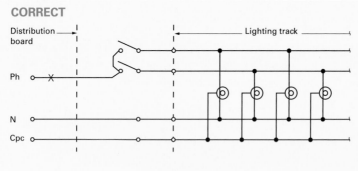

CORRECT

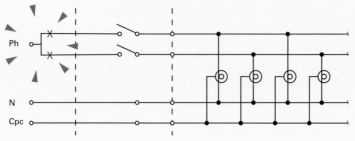

NOT ACCEPTABLE – BORROWED NEUTRAL

Regulation 14 (from the Electricity at Work (EWR) Regulations)

Work on or near live conductors

No person shall be engaged in any work activity on or so near any live conductor (other than one suitably covered with insulating material so as to prevent danger) that danger may arise unless -

a) it is unreasonable in all the circumstances for it to be dead; and

b) it is reasonable in all the circumstances for him to be at work on or near it while it is live; and

c) suitable precautions (including where necessary the provision of suitable protective equipment) are taken to prevent injury.

Regulation 314-01-04

Where an installation comprises more than one final circuit, each final circuit shall be connected to a separate way in a distribution board. The wiring of each final circuit shall be electrically separate from that of every other final circuit, so as to prevent the indirect energising of a final circuit intended to be isolated.

Neutrals at consumer units and distribution boards

Neutral conductors must be clearly identified by position or labelling at a distribution board or consumer unit.

Snag 29

Sometimes it is found that the neutral conductors of outgoing circuits have been indiscriminately connected at a consumer unit or a distribution board. This can lead to danger if, as a result, an incorrect neutral is disconnected

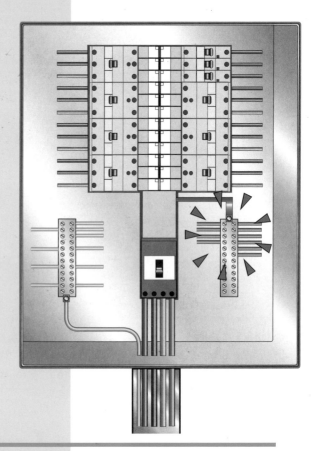

Solution

Neutral conductors must be so arranged or marked that they can be identified for inspection, testing, repair or alteration of the installation (Regulations 314-01-04 and 514-01-02 refer).

In a single-phase installation, neutral conductors will normally be connected to the neutral bar in sequence. For example the neutral conductor of the first final circuit will be connected to the first terminal, the second to the second etc. so that additional marking would not be needed.

In a three-phase and neutral installation, identification of neutral conductors can be difficult if the arrangement of terminals on the neutral bar does not correspond exactly with that of the phase terminals. This can lead to danger if, as a result, an incorrect neutral is disconnected. In such a case, additional marking of the conductors by, for example, numbering, would be needed.

Some manufacturers provide a neutral bar chart in addition to the chart for protective devices.

A clear indication of the neutral connections is necessary and should always be provided when the layout of the neutral bar differs from the layout of the protective devices.

Regulation 314-01-04

Where an installation comprises more than one final circuit, each final circuit shall be connected to a separate way in a distribution board. The wiring of each final circuit shall be electrically separate from that of every other final circuit, so as to prevent the indirect energising of a final circuit intended to be isolated.

Regulation 514-01-02

As far as is reasonably practicable, wiring shall be so arranged or marked that it can be identified for inspection, testing, repair or alteration of the installation.

Accessories mounted on wooden blocks

Older installations may include accessories mounted on wooden blocks

Snag 30

Older properties often have accessories mounted on wooden blocks. Often, the wooden block forms part of the enclosure for the unsheathed cores and terminations of the cables connecting to the accessory. In such a case there can be a greater risk of fire in the event of a fault such as a poor connection.

Depending on the characteristics of the particular wood from which the block was made, such an enclosure may not satisfy the current requirements of BS 7671 in respect of ignitability.

Solution

The accessories in question must be replaced such that every termination or joint in a live conductor (which includes neutral conductors) is made in a suitable enclosure. (Regulation 526-03-02 refers).

Regulation 526-03-02

Every termination and joint in a live conductor or a PEN conductor shall be made within one of the following or a combination thereof:

(i) a suitable accessory complying with the appropriate British Standard

(ii) an equipment enclosure complying with the appropriate British Standard

(iii) a suitable enclosure of material complying with the relevant glow-wire test requirements of BS 6458-2.1

(iv) an enclosure formed or completed with building material considered to be non-combustible when tested to BS 476-4

(v) an enclosure formed or completed by part of the building structure, having the ignitability characteristic 'P' as specified in BS 476 Part 5.

Cable damage by vermin

Damage to cables from the gnawing of rats, mice and squirrels is a relatively common occurrence.

Snag 31

In some locations cables can be susceptible to damage by vermin.

Damage can occur over considerable lengths of cable where rodents have gnawed away the sheath and insulation, resulting in exposure of the conductors.

Where exposed conductors are surrounded by rodents' nesting materials, which are generally combustible, there is a risk of fire. There is also a risk of shock to persons from direct contact with an exposed live conductor.

Evidence shows that rodents are not uniquely attracted to one type of cable. All types of cable, for example: thermoplastic (pvc), rubber and lead sheathed cables, seem susceptible to attack.

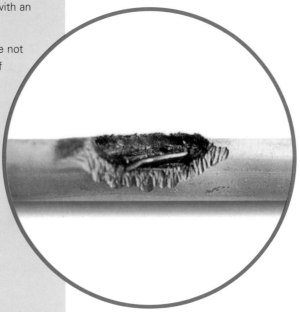

Wiring Systems

Solution

Where cables are installed in areas that are, or are liable to be, inhabited by rodents, such as might be found in farm buildings and the roof voids and cellars of certain older properties, the wiring system must be capable of resisting damage caused by gnawing. It is advisable, therefore, to select a wiring system such as one of the following:

- Steel conduit, or trunking

- Mineral-insulated, metal-sheathed cables

- Steel-wire armoured cables

- Thermoplastic (pvc) sheathed cables having galvanized steel braid covering

- Steel capping to protect short exposed runs of thermoplastic (pvc) insulated and sheathed cables.

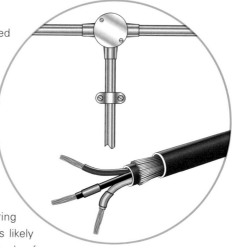

Alternatively, if the use of such wiring systems is impracticable, cables are less likely to be attacked by rodents if they are attached as far up a wall as possible, or, where installed in a roof void, fixed to the underside of the roof structure.

It is worth noting that enclosures of electrical switchgear, accessories and wiring systems (such as trunking), etc should be free of any openings through which rodents could enter and build nests and cause damage to cables.

Manufacturers of cables have said that there is no wholly effective means of prevention, and that if repellents are incorporated in the cable sheath they would almost certainly be toxic and therefore unsuitable for handling in cable factories, and might also be a danger to people handling the finished cable.

Regulation 522-10-01 (Presence of fauna(AL))

Where expected conditions constitute a hazard (AL2), the wiring system shall be selected accordingly or special protective measures shall be adopted.

Grommets at metal back boxes

Metal enclosures such as accessory boxes, distribution boards and consumer units can have sharp edges at cable entry points which can cut into the sheath and insulation of an unprotected cable.

Snag 32

Where an unprotected cable such as a twin and earth pvc-insulated and pvc-sheathed cable enters a metal enclosure, the installation designer or installer must ensure the cable is protected from damage from sharp edges.

Damage to a cable may result in the risk of electric shock or fire.

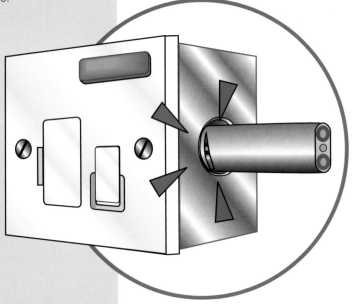

Solution

Wiring systems must be selected and erected to minimize mechanical damage during installation, use and maintenance. Regulation 522-06-01 refers. Cable sheaths must be protected from any sharp edges along the whole of their length as well as at the entry point into the item of switchgear or accessory. The cable may be protected from damage by one or more of the methods of:

- deburring,

- providing suitable physical protection, or

- providing an appropriate grommet.

Failure to provide a grommet where a cable, such as a twin and cpc flat cable, enters a metal back box is not, in its own right, a deficiency, providing the cable sheath is adequately protected against damage from any sharp edges.

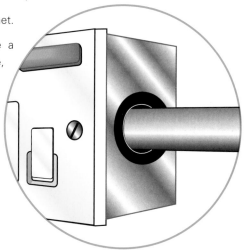

Regulation 522-06-01

Wiring systems shall be selected and erected so as to minimize mechanical damage e.g. damage due to impact, abrasion, penetration, compression or tension, during installation, use and maintenance.

Cables embedded in thin walls or partitions

An unprotected cable embedded in a wall or partition at a depth of less than 50 mm from the surfaces can be vulnerable to penetration by nails and screws.

Snag 33

A nail or a screw penetrating a cable can lead to the dangers of electric shock or fire.

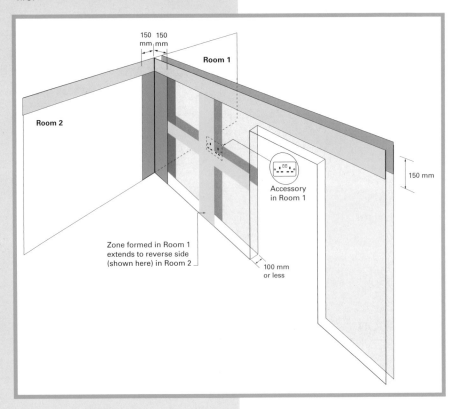

150 mm   150 mm

Room 1

Room 2

Accessory in Room 1

150 mm

Zone formed in Room 1 extends to reverse side (shown here) in Room 2

100 mm or less

Solution

It is important that cable runs are properly planned and that the cables are installed in such a manner as to afford compliance with the requirements of BS 7671.

Section 522 of BS 7671 requires that where a cable such as a pvc insulated and sheathed (pvc/pvc) cable is concealed in a wall or partition at a depth of less than 50 mm from either or both of the surfaces, then:

Either the cable must be installed:

- [ ] in a zone within 150 mm of the top of the wall or partition, or
- [ ] in a zone within 150 mm of an angle formed by adjoining walls or partitions, or
- [ ] in a zone running either horizontally or vertically to a point, accessory or switchgear to which the cable is connected
- [ ] this zone now extends to the reverse side of the wall or partition of 100 mm thickness or less if the location of the point, accessory or switchgear can be determined from that reverse side

or, alternatively, the cable must:

- incorporate an earthed metallic covering complying with the requirements of the Regulations for a circuit protective conductor of the circuit concerned, or

- be enclosed in earthed conduit, trunking or ducting satisfying the requirements of the Regulations for a protective conductor, or

- be enclosed by mechanical protection sufficient to prevent penetration of the cable by nails, screws or the like, or

- be of insulated concentric construction.

Safe zones

When planning cable routes and installing cables in order to meet the safe zone condition, it is essential to consider both surfaces of the wall or partition where the wall or partition is less than 100 mm thick and there is ready access to both sides.

For example, consider a building where proprietary panels less than 100 mm thick have been used for partition walls where access is available to both sides. Such panels usually incorporate service holes, positioned midway between the surfaces, in which electrical cables are intended to be run to switches, socket-outlets and other accessories. It is clear that cables installed in this manner will not be more than 50 mm from either surface of the partition. Therefore, unless the accessory is installed in a zone within 150 mm of the top of the partition or in a zone within 150 mm of an angle formed by two adjoining walls or partitions, an unprotected cable such as a twin and earth pvc/pvc cable may be connected to an accessory only in a zone running horizontally or vertically and this zone now extends to the reverse side of the wall or partition.

Alternatively the cable used needs to incorporate, or be provided with, suitable mechanical protection.

Cables incorporating an earthed armour or metal sheath

Where a cable such as mineral insulated copper sheathed (MICS) or steel wire armoured (SWA) is employed, the earthed metallic sheath or armouring of the cable is required to meet the requirements for a protective conductor for the circuit concerned relating to electrical continuity and cross-sectional area.

The use of the metallic covering of a cable as a circuit protective conductor is intended to ensure that it will not be possible for a nail, screw or the like to make contact with a live conductor of the cable without first coming into good electrical contact with the earthed metallic covering (by piercing), thus providing a direct path for earth fault current to flow to cause automatic disconnection of the circuit concerned.

Enclosure in earthed conduit, trunking or ducting

In principle, an earthed steel conduit, trunking or ducting utilizes the same method of protection as a cable with an earthed metallic covering and, by construction, provides a higher degree of mechanical protection.

Mechanical protection sufficient to prevent penetration

It is permitted for a cable to be provided with mechanical protection sufficient to prevent penetration of the cable by nails, screws or the like. The mechanical protection, normally metallic, need not be earthed. However, it has to be recognized that, in some circumstances, such mechanical protection may not be sufficient to ensure that a cable cannot be penetrated (for example where fixing methods of other trades include shot-fired nails) and would therefore be unacceptable.

Insulated concentric construction

The use of an insulated concentric cable effectively provides the same method of protection as a cable having an earthed metallic covering. In order for a nail or screw to make contact with the live conductor it would first have to penetrate the combined protective and neutral (PEN) conductor (or, if the cable is of the split concentric type, either the neutral or protective conductor).

Protection against damage during construction works

Cables run on walls that will subsequently be plastered must be protected against damage (such as damage caused by the plasterer's trowel).

Locations containing a bath or shower

With permitted exceptions, surface wiring systems and wiring systems embedded in a wall at a depth not exceeding 50 mm in zones 0,1 or 2 of a location containing a bath or shower are subject to limitations. Regulations 601-07 refer.

Regulation 522-06-06

A cable concealed in a wall or partition at a depth of less than 50 mm from the surfaces of the wall or partition shall:

(i)   incorporate an earthed metallic covering which complies with the requirements of these Regulations for a protective conductor of the circuit concerned, the cable complying with BS 5467, BS 6346, BS 6724, BS 7846, BS EN 60702-1 or BS 8436, or

(ii) be of insulated concentric construction complying with BS 4553-1, BS 4553-2, or BS 4553-3, or

(iii) be enclosed in earthed conduit, trunking or ducting satisfying the requirements of these Regulations for a protective conductor, or be mechanically protected sufficient to prevent penetration of the cable by nails, screws and the like, or

(iv) be installed in a zone within 150 mm from the top of the wall or partition or within 150 mm of an angle formed by two adjoining walls or partitions. Where the cable is connected to a point, accessory or switchgear on any surface of the wall or partition, the cable may be installed in a zone either horizontally or vertically, to the point, accessory or switchgear. Where the location of the accessory, point or switchgear can be determined from the reverse side, a zone formed on one side of a wall of 100 mm thickness or less or partition of 100 mm thickness or less extends to the reverse side.

Regulation 522-06-07

Deleted by amendment 2 to BS 7671.

Two two-way switching circuits

In this particular snag, two two-way switching circuits have been run using twin and earth cables.

Snag 34

The circuits have been run entirely in twin and earth flat cable, as shown.

The problem with this arrangement is one of borrowed neutrals.

This is an example of one of the most dangerous practices that can be committed. 'Borrowing' the neutral of another circuit creates a dangerous trap for any electrician carrying out maintenance work or other installation alterations or extension work in the future.

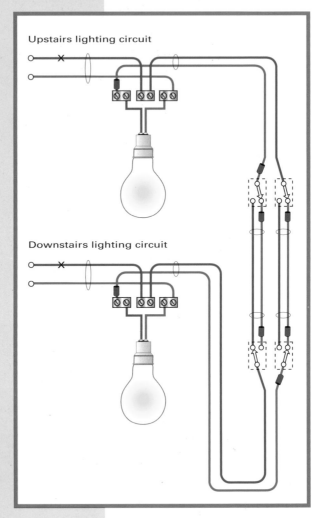

Upstairs lighting circuit

Downstairs lighting circuit

Note that in the diagram, for clarity, the circuit protective conductors are not shown.

Solution

Two separate circuits supply the ground and first floor lighting of a two- storey house. Two-way switching is provided in the hall and the upstairs landing for the hall and landing lights.

The downstairs luminaire takes its supply from the upstairs lighting circuit but its neutral connection is made to the downstairs circuit.

The upstairs luminaire takes its supply from the downstairs lighting circuit but its neutral connection is from the upstairs circuit.

The neutral must be taken from the same circuit, never from another circuit.

The circuits must be rewired using cables such as three-core and earth flat cables to interconnect the two-way switches.

Where an installation comprises more than one final circuit, each final circuit must be connected to a separate way in a distribution board. The wiring of each final circuit must be electrically separate from that of every other final circuit, so as to prevent the indirect energising of a final circuit intended to be isolated. This is necessary not only to avoid danger during a fault but also to facilitate safe operation, inspection, testing and maintenance (Regulation 314-01-04 refers).

Upstairs lighting circuit

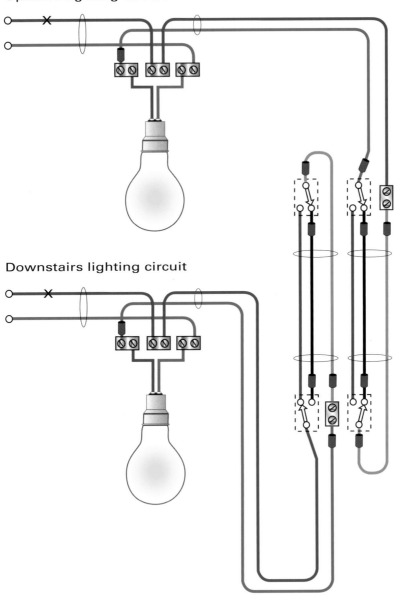

Downstairs lighting circuit

Note that in the diagram, for clarity, the circuit protective conductors are not shown.

The neutral is, by definition, a live conductor (so that Regulation 14 of the Electricity at Work Regulations is applicable and should always be treated as live until it is isolated and proved to be dead. It is important that where it is necessary to disconnect the neutral conductor, it is undertaken with insulated tools, and that the neutral conductor as with the live conductor and any other conductors is not touched until proved dead.

Regulation 14 (from the Electricity at Work (EWR) Regulations)

Work on or near live conductors

No person shall be engaged in any work activity on or so near any live conductor (other than one suitably covered with insulating material so as to prevent danger) that danger may arise unless -

a) it is unreasonable in all the circumstances for it to be dead; and

b) it is reasonable in all the circumstances for him to be at work on or near it while it is live; and

c) suitable precautions (including where necessary the provision of suitable protective equipment) are taken to prevent injury.

Regulation 314-01-04

Where an installation comprises more than one final circuit, each final circuit shall be connected to a separate way in a distribution board. The wiring of each final circuit shall be electrically separate from that of every other final circuit, so as to prevent the indirect energising of a final circuit intended to be isolated.

Wiring above batten and board ceilings

Cables routed above batten and board ceilings must be protected against mechanical damage.

Snag 35

Damage can occur to cables installed above a batten and board ceiling, which may be caused by a ceiling fixing nail, leading to danger of fire or electric shock.

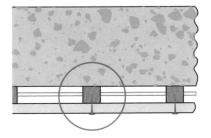

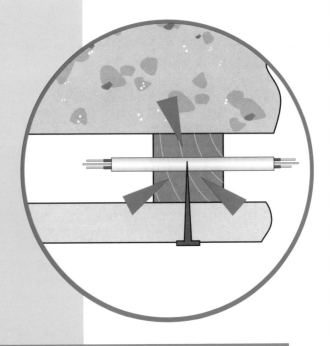

Solution

A 'batten and board' ceiling consists of ceiling boards fixed to wooden battens on the underside of a solid intermediate floor or roof slab (such as concrete), and is often considered to be a convenient place to install cables.

A cable passing through a ceiling batten within a batten and board ceiling must do so at a height of least 50 mm from the bottom of the batten unless certain alternative conditions are met (Regulation 522-06-05 refers).

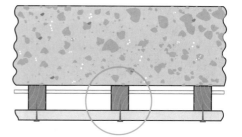

To comply with Regulation 522-06-05, a cable installed within the void of a batten and board ceiling must be so positioned that it is not liable to be damaged by contact with the ceiling or its fixings. In addition, where the cable passes through a timber batten within the ceiling construction, the regulation requires the cable to:

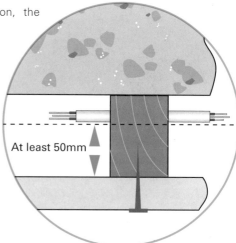

At least 50mm

(a) Be at least 50 mm measured vertically from the bottom of the batten, or alternatively to comply with one of the following requirements:

(b) incorporate an earthed armour or metal sheath suitable for use as a protective conductor,

(c) be of insulated concentric construction

(d) be protected by enclosure in earthed steel conduit securely supported, or

(e) have equivalent mechanical protection sufficient to prevent penetration of the cable by nails, screws and the like (see also Regulation 471-13-04(v)).

For cables to be installed in accordance with condition (a), co-ordination with the builder and/or building designer may be necessary. It is common practice to use 38 mm battens, which with 12 mm plasterboard does not leave sufficient space for the cables. Discussions with the architect or builder should take place at an early stage. Where such provisions cannot be made, one (or more) of the conditions (b) to (e) must be met.

A word of caution regarding condition (e), which normally involves mechanically protecting cables where they pass through wooden battens. Protection is normally provided by means such as short sections of metal conduit (or a metal plate), which, according to Regulation 471-13-04(v), do not have to be earthed. In some circumstances, such mechanical protection may not be sufficient to ensure that a cable cannot be penetrated by a nail or screw or the like, and is therefore unacceptable because it does not afford compliance with Regulation 522-06-05. For example, where fixing methods of other trades include shot-fired nails, steel conduit or a metal plate of similar thickness may not prevent penetration. Likewise, some proprietary metal plates intended for fixing to the surface of a joist or batten where a cable passes through are too thin to prevent penetration of the cable or even to make the person driving the nails aware that there is an intended barrier.

Cable installed with a cross-battened ceiling construction.

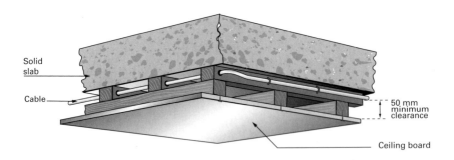

Solid slab

Cable

50 mm minimum clearance

Ceiling board

Regulation 471-13-04 (part of)

It is permissible to dispense with protective measures against indirect contact in the following instances:

(v) inaccessible lengths of metal conduit not exceeding 150 mm.

Regulation 522-06-05

A cable installed under a floor or above a ceiling shall be run in such a position that it is not liable to be damaged by contact with the floor or the ceiling or their fixings. A cable passing through a timber joist within a floor or ceiling construction or through a ceiling support (e.g. under floorboards), shall:

(i) Be at least 50 mm measured vertically from the top, or bottom as appropriate, of the joist or batten, or

(ii) incorporate an earthed armour or metal sheath suitable for use as a protective conductor, or shall be of insulated concentric construction, or shall be protected by enclosure in earthed steel conduit securely supported, or by equivalent mechanical protection sufficient to prevent penetration of the cable by nails, screws and the like (see also Regulation 471-13-04(v)).

Drilling and notching of timber joists

Holes and notches can compromise the load bearing integrity of joists.

Snag 36

The load bearing capacity may be seriously affected when drilling or notching a timber joist.

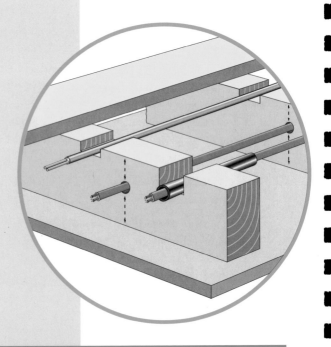

Solution

Practical advice is given in Approved Document A for meeting the requirements of the Building Regulations, in respect of notches and holes in floor and roof joists in single family houses. Approved Document A is issued by the Department of the Environment and the Welsh Office. Extracts are as follows:

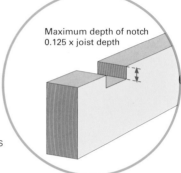

Maximum depth of notch
0.125 x joist depth

1B6 Notches and holes in simply supported floor and roof joists should be within the following limits.

a. notches should be no deeper than 0.125 times the depth of a joist and should not be cut closer to the support than 0.07 of the span, nor further away than 0.25 times the span, and

b. holes should be no greater diameter than 0.25 times the depth of the joist; should be drilled at the neutral axis; and should be not less than 3 diameters (centre to centre) apart; and should be located between 0.25 and 0.4 times the span from the support.

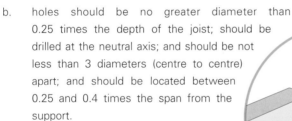

Maximum diameter
0.25 x joist depth

No notches or holes should be cut in roof rafters, other than at supports where the rafter may be birdsmouthed to a depth not exceeding 0.33 times the rafter depth.

Note that right-angled adapters or drills can be obtained.

Regulation 522-12-03

No wiring system shall penetrate an element of building construction which is intended to be load bearing unless the integrity of the load-bearing element can be assured after such penetration.

Cable clips

Cable clips must be used in the manner intended. Securing two cables, edge-on, under one clip would not be considered good workmanship.

Snag 37

If two flat twin and earth cables are secured using a single cable clip, laid edge-on as shown, mechanical damage is likely.

Compression can occur due to the clip being hammered in too far.

The sheath may be split by a hammer blow, or the un-insulated protective conductor may be forced through the insulation of the lower conductor, causing either a phase to earth or neutral to earth fault.

A phase to earth fault is likely to be detected by the overcurrent protective device, whereas, in the absence of RCD protection, the neutral to earth fault may persist indefinitely, resulting in a risk of fire.

Furthermore, the cables are no longer clipped direct and thermal considerations may be different from those intended by the designer.

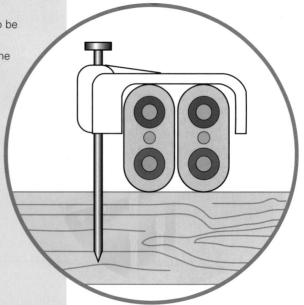

Wiring Systems

Solution

The clips are designed to hold and not unduly compress the intended cable when hammered home. They should be used in the manner intended. Good workmanship and proper materials must be used (Regulation 133-01-01 refers). Different sizes of clips are available to accommodate various cross-sectional areas (csa) and shapes (ie: circular or twin and earth).

Wiring systems must be erected so as to minimize mechanical damage e.g. damage due to compression or impact during installation. (Regulation 522-06-01 refers).

Where two cables are to be run next to each other, they should be individually clipped as shown.

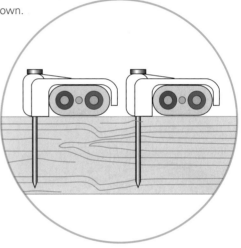

Regulation 133-01-01

Good workmanship and proper materials shall be used.

Regulation 522-06-01

Wiring systems shall be selected and erected so as to minimize mechanical damage e.g. damage due to impact, abrasion, penetration, compression or tension during installation, use and maintenance.

Making provision for the future connection of luminaires

An installation must not be energized unless cables are both properly terminated and enclosed.

Snag 38

A snag can easily arise with wall lights, downlighters, and the like.

Consider a new installation where the wall lights have not yet been selected yet it is required to energize the installation to have the other lights operational.

It is not acceptable for an energized cable to emerge from a wall merely terminated in a taped-up connector block. A risk of electric shock exists.

The use of electrical insulating tape as the sole means of enclosure for terminations is not acceptable.

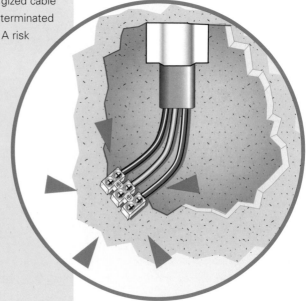

Wiring Systems

Solution

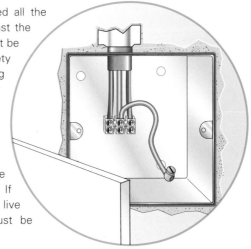

When the lighting circuit is energized all the measures necessary to protect against the hazards of electric shock and fire must be in place. The requirements for safety (which includes inspection and testing prior to putting in to use) apply irrespective of the time that may elapse before the remaining luminaires are fitted.

If the lighting circuit is to be energized, the fixed wiring of the circuit must be terminated into a suitable enclosure. If cables are left unterminated the live (phase and neutral) conductors must be securely isolated from the supply.

Every electrical connection (joint or termination) in a live conductor or PEN conductor is required to be made within a suitable enclosure, or a combination of them (Regulation 526-03-02 refers). The Regulation also applies to connections in extra-low voltage circuits.

A suitable ceiling rose, luminaire supporting coupler (LSCs), junction box or accessory enclosure can be used to terminate fixed wiring. Where the physical size of the connection arrangement is an issue (as is often the case with a wall light), an architrave box with a blank cover can provide a suitable enclosure.

Regulation 526-03-02

Every termination and joint in a live conductor or a PEN conductor shall be made within one of the following or a combination thereof:

    (i)   a suitable accessory complying with the appropriate British Standard

    (ii) an equipment enclosure complying with the appropriate British Standard

    (iii) a suitable enclosure of material complying with the relevant glow-wire test requirements of BS 6458-2.1

    (iv) an enclosure formed or completed with building material considered to be non-combustible when tested to BS 476-4

    (v) an enclosure formed or completed by part of the building structure, having the ignitability characteristic 'P' as specified in BS 476 Part 5.

Fuse in the neutral conductor

The circuits of older installations may be fitted with fuses in the neutral conductors.

Snag 39

Separate fuses installed in the phase and neutral conductors of a circuit can pose a risk of electric shock in the event that, under fault conditions, the fuse in the neutral conductor operates leaving phase voltage still being supplied to the faulty circuit.

Up to the 1950s, the circuits of many installations had a fuse in both the neutral conductor and the phase conductor. This is a potentially dangerous situation for a.c. installations because, in the event of a phase to neutral overload or short-circuit, there is a 50% chance that the fuse in the neutral conductor will operate, rather than the fuse in the phase conductor. When this happens, the phase conductor is not automatically disconnected from the faulty circuit creating a danger for the person called on to investigate the fault.

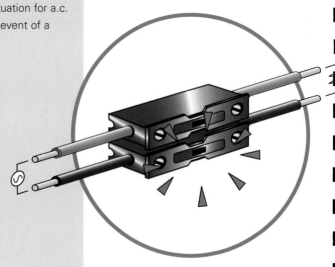

Solution

The fuse and the fuse-holder in the neutral conductor
should be physically removed (Regulations 131-13-01 and
530-01-02 refer). The circuit, and indeed the
installation, must be checked for electrical
safety. The inspector should bear in mind
that the installation probably dates from
the 1950s or before.

Regulation 131-13-01

A single-pole fuse, switch or circuit-breaker shall be inserted in the phase conductor
only.

Regulation 530-01-02

No fuse or, excepting where linked, switch or circuit-breaker shall be inserted in the
neutral conductor of TN or TT systems.

PVC cables above suspended ceilings

The space above a suspended ceiling offers a useful void for the installation of electricity, water, gas, heating and other services

Snag 40

The grid of light metal bars, usually having an inverted 'T' section, into which ceiling tiles, recessed luminaires (light fittings) and ventilation grilles etc are installed is not considered adequate and appropriate support for installing, say, pvc insulated and sheathed cables. Consequently, such cables should not be laid directly on the metal framework for the following reasons:-

- The cable is liable to be damaged, both during installation and later, by the sharp edges of the grid, or a cable may become trapped between a ceiling tile and the grid, possibly where other trades have carried out work in connection with the ceiling or other services routed above.

- The suspended ceiling grid may not have been designed to take the additional weight of cables, and may deform or collapse as a result.

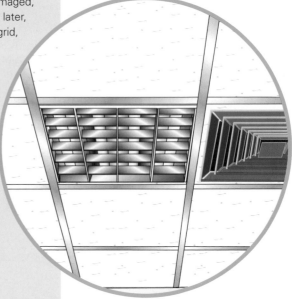

Wiring Systems

Solution

All cables for fixed wiring are required to be properly supported within a suspended ceiling void. This can be achieved in a number of ways to ensure that the cables are kept well away from the grid and from other services.

For example, a designer should consider:

- fixing the cables to the underside of the ceiling

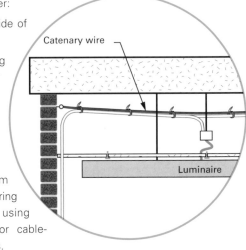

Catenary wire

Luminaire

- providing a conduit, trunking system or cable tray (metallic or non-metallic) fixed at suitable spacings to the building structure above the ceiling, or to walls or other structural elements.

- providing a catenary system (shown right), to which the wiring system may be attached using proprietary clips, cable-ties or cable-hangers at appropriate intervals.

- attaching the cables by suitable clips or cable ties to ceiling support rods.

Connections to luminaires should be made by sheathed flexible cords from ceiling roses or Luminaire Supporting Couplers (LSCs) located as closely as possible above each lighting point so as to avoid fortuitous contact of the flexible cord with the framework.

Regulation 522-06-01

Wiring systems shall be selected and erected so as to minimize mechanical damage e.g. damage due to impact, abrasion, penetration, compression or tension, during installation, use and maintenance.

Regulation 522-08-01

A wiring system shall be selected and erected so as to minimize during installation, use and maintenance, damage to the sheath and insulation of cables and insulated conductors and their terminations.

Wiring systems in lift shafts

The only wiring system permitted in a lift shaft is that relating to the lift installation

Snag 41

Contractors should be aware that it is not permitted to run cables in a lift shaft.

This restriction on the use of the lift shaft is mainly due to considerations of fire risk and to the problems of gaining safe access for inspection, testing and maintenance of equipment not related to the lift installation.

Solution

The only wiring permitted in a lift shaft is that relating to the lift installation, such as lift shaft lighting (Regulation 528-02-06 refers). Lift shaft lighting is often run in conduit.

Wiring, other than that relating to the lift installation, must be removed and rerouted.

Regulation 528-02-06

No cable shall be run in a lift (or hoist) shaft unless it forms part of the lift installation as defined in BS 5655.

Flexible cords and cables

Flexible cords and cables may, under appropriate conditions, be used as fixed wiring.

Snag 42

The Wiring Regulations used not to permit the use of flexible cords as fixed wiring unless contained in an enclosure affording protection against mechanical damage. However, the position has now changed since the 16th edition of the Wiring Regulations was published.

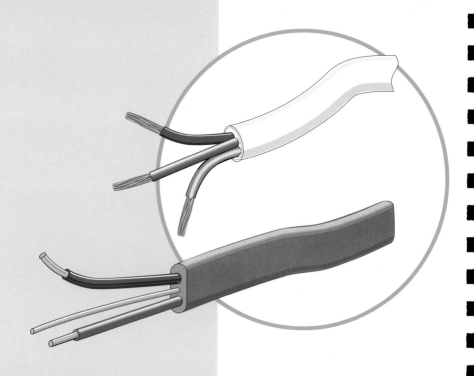

Solution

Flexible cables may be used for fixed wiring provided the applicable requirements are met. Regulation 521-01-04 permits the use of flexible cables and cords for fixed wiring. The applicable requirements include the general requirements relating to cables such as cross-sectional area of conductors, consideration of the connections (an adequate connection must be ensured - Section 526 of BS 7671 refers) and the flexible cable or cord must be properly routed and adequately supported. The flexible cable or cord may require more cleats than an equivalent solid-core cable. Every core of a flexible cable or cord must be identifiable either by colour and/or numbering and lettering with certain permitted exceptions. (Regulations 514-03-01 and 514-06-01 refer). Where identification is to be by colour, the cores are to be identified as indicated in Table 51 of BS 7671.

Definitions

Flexible cable: *A cable whose structure and materials make it suitable to be flexed while in service*

Flexible cord: *A flexible cable in which the cross-sectional area of each conductor does not exceed 4 mm^2.*

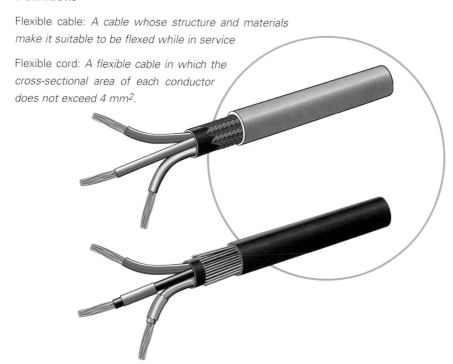

TABLE 51 - Identification of conductors

Function		Colour	Alpha numeric
Protective conductors		Green-and-yellow	
Functional earthing conductor		Cream	
a.c. power circuit[1]			
Phase of single-phase circuit		Brown	L
Neutral of single- or three-phase circuit		Blue	N
Phase 1 of three-phase a.c. circuit		Brown	L1
Phase 2 of three-phase a.c. circuit		Black	L2
Phase 3 of three-phase a.c. circuit		Grey	L3
Two-wire unearthed d.c. power circuit			
Positive of two-wire circuit		Brown	L+
Negative of two-wire circuit		Grey	L-
Two-wire earthed d.c. power circuit			
Positive (of negative earthed) circuit		Brown	L+
Negative (of negative earthed) circuit[2]		Blue	M
Positive (of positive earthed) circuit[2]		Blue	M
Negative (of positive earthed) circuit		Grey	L-
Three-wire d.c. power circuit			
Outer positive of two-wire circuit derived from three-wire system		Brown	L+
Outer negative of two-wire circuit derived from three-wire system		Grey	L-
Positive of three-wire circuit		Brown	L+
Mid-wire of three-wire circuit[2][3]		Blue	M
Negative of three-wire circuit		Grey	L-
Control circuits, ELV and other applications			
Phase conductor		Grey	L

	Brown		Orange	White
	Black		Yellow	Pink, or
	Red		Violet	Turquoise

Function		Colour	Alpha numeric
Neutral or mid-wire[4]		Blue	N or M

NOTES:
[1] Power circuits include lighting circuits.
[2] M identifies either the mid wire of a three-wire d.c. circuit, or the earthed conductor of a two-wire earthed dc circuit.
[3] Only the middle wire of three-wire circuits may be earthed.
[4] An earthed PELV conductor is blue.

Regulation 514-03-01

Except where identification is not required by Regulation 514-06, cores of cables shall be identified by:

    (i)   colour as required by Regulation 514-04 and /or

    (ii) lettering and/or numbering as required by Regulation 514-05.

Regulation 514-06-01

Identification by colour or marking is not required for:

    (i)   concentric conductors of cables

    (ii) metal sheath or armour of cables when used as a protective conductor

    (iii) bare conductors where permanent identification is not practicable

    (iv) extraneous-conductive-parts used as a protective conductor

    (v) exposed-conductive-parts used as a protective conductor.

Regulation 521-01-04

A flexible cable or flexible cord shall be used for fixed wiring only where the relevant provisions of the Regulations are met.

---

snags and solutions © NICEIC

Socket-outlets

The relative positions of the terminals at the back of different makes of socket-outlet may be different.

Snag 43

The terminals of different makes and even different models of socket-outlet from the same manufacturer can be positioned differently.

Inadvertent wrong connection can result, particularly where the contractor is familiar with one model from one manufacturer and is then called on to fit a different type.

Incorrect polarity could present a risk of electric shock.

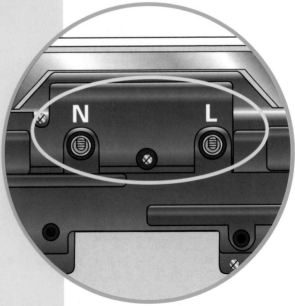

Solution

British Standards specify the relative location of the contacts in the socket-outlet but the disposition of the terminals is not laid down and can be arranged to suit the ease of manufacture, or just the whim of the designer. The function of each terminal must, or course, be marked but this does not entirely overcome the problem if terminals are transposed on different types of socket-outlet.

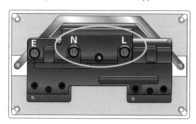

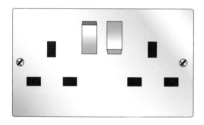
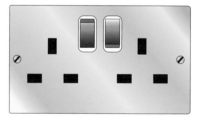

New, repositioned or repaired socket-outlets must not be put into service until the required verification procedures have been completed and it has been established that, as far as reasonably practicable, the requirements of BS 7671 have been met. (Regulation 133-02-01 refers)

It is unsafe and therefore unacceptable to energize a socket-outlet final circuit and then to plug in a socket-outlet tester to check for basic wiring faults. For example, most socket-outlet testers are unable to indicate whether neutral and protective conductors are transposed. Furthermore, simple* socket-outlet testers will indicate certain wiring faults but cannot prove the adequacy of protective earthing arrangements.

*   It is important to distinguish between simple socket-outlet testers that have been available for many years and are in widespread use, and certain more advanced designs. Most simple socket-outlet testers basically indicate wiring faults. There is at least one socket-outlet tester available which is a more sophisticated and complex device which will, in addition, detect and display various bands of earth fault loop impedance. Such a device is not considered to be a 'simple' socket-outlet tester for the purposes of this Snag.

The requirements applicable to the verification of a newly-installed socket-outlet include:

Requirement	Applicable Regulation
The socket-outlet must be correctly selected and erected, undamaged and not defective	712-01-02
Conductors properly connected and cables properly routed	712-01-03
Continuity test of protective conductor	713-02-01
Continuity test of ring final circuit conductors and protective conductor	713-03-01
Insulation resistance test	713-04
Polarity test	713-09
Earth fault loop impedance	713-11
Functional test	713-13-02

Regulation 133-02-01

On completion of an installation or an addition or alteration to an installation, appropriate inspection and testing shall be carried out to verify, so far as is reasonably practicable that the requirements of this standard (BS 7671) have been met.

Regulation 712-01-02 (part of)

The inspection shall be made to verify that the installed electrical equipment is:

(ii) correctly selected and erected in accordance with the Regulations, and

(iii) not visibly damaged or defective so as to impair safety.

Regulation 712-01-03 (part of)

The inspection shall include at least the checking of the following items, where relevant to the installation and, where necessary, during erection:

(i) connection of conductors

(vi) correct connection of accessories and equipment.

Regulation 713-02-01

A continuity test shall be made. It is recommended that the test be carried out with a supply having a no-load voltage between 4 V and 24 V, d.c. or a.c., and a short-circuit current of not less than 200 mA.

Regulation 713-03-01

A test shall be made to verify the continuity of each conductor including the protective conductor, of every ring final circuit.

Regulation 713-04-01 (part of)

The insulation resistance between live conductors and between each live conductor and Earth shall be measured before the installation is connected to the supply.

TABLE 71A
Minimum values of insulation resistance

Circuit nominal voltage (V)	Test voltage d.c. (V)	Minimum insulation resistance (MΩ)
Up to and including 500 V with the exception of SELV and PELV systems	500	0.5

Regulation 713-09-01 (part of)

A test of polarity shall be made and it shall be verified that:
  (iii) wiring has been correctly connected to socket-outlets and similar accessories.

Regulation 713-11-01 (part of)

Where protective measures are used which require a knowledge of earth fault loop impedance, the relevant impedances shall be measured, or determined by an alternative method.

Regulation 713-13-02 (summary)

Assemblies shall be subjected to a functional test. *See Regulation for full details.*

Crimp connectors

A proper electrical connection must be made when crimp connectors are used

Snag 44

A poor connection may result in excessive temperatures likely to cause burns, fires and other injurious effects.

Common problems with crimped connections include:

- Not using the proper crimping tool resulting in a mechanically poor joint

- Not using the correct size of lug resulting in a loose connection

- Not stripping back enough insulation and crimping on to the insulation resulting in an electrically poor joint

- Crimping two or more times, thereby weakening the connector

- Failing to properly enclose the connection, where required.

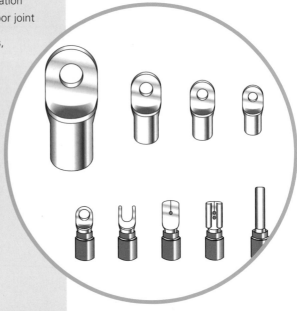

Wiring Systems

Solution

Compression-type, or 'crimp-type' connectors are acceptable for terminations and joints in electrical installations in compliance with Regulation 526-01-01. A crimped joint must be properly made using an appropriate sized lug and the correct crimping tool.

Compression-type connectors are available ranging in size from those suitable for 1 mm^2 cables to those suitable for 1,000 mm^2 cables. BS 4579-1: 1970 gives details of compression connectors. To ensure an effective crimp, hand tools are available for the smaller sizes and an hydraulic tool is required for the larger sizes.

BS 4579-1:1970 is entitled: *Specification for performance of mechanical and compression joints in electric cable and wire connectors. Compression joints in copper conductors* and covers the requirements for the performance of general application compression joints for use with copper and copper alloy conductors up to 1000 mm^2 cross-sectional area operating below 85°C.

The connection(s) must be properly enclosed as required by Regulation 526-03-02.

Crimped connections are not required to be accessible for inspection, testing and maintenance; hence such connections may not be inspected throughout the lifetime of the installation and therefore great care must be taken to ensure they are properly made (Regulation 526-04-01 relates).

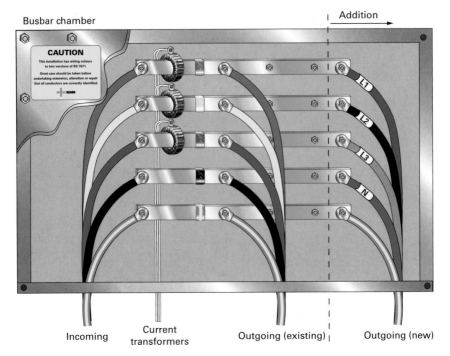

Busbar chamber

Addition

CAUTION

This installation has wiring colours to two versions of BS 7671.

Great care should be taken before undertaking extension, alteration or repair that all conductors are correctly identified.

L1
L2
L3
N

Incoming

Current transformers

Outgoing (existing)

Outgoing (new)

Crimped joints must be properly made using an appropriate sized lug and the correct crimping tool.

Regulation 133-01-04

Every electrical joint and connection shall be of proper construction as regards conductance, insulation, mechanical strength and protection

Regulation 526-01-01

Every connection between conductors and between a conductor and equipment shall provide durable electrical continuity and adequate mechanical strength (see Other mechanical stresses, Regulation 522-08).

Regulation 526-02-01

The selection of the means of connection shall take account, as appropriate, of the following:

(i)   the material of the conductor and its insulation

(ii) the number and shape of the wires forming the conductor

(iii) the cross-sectional area of the conductor

(iv) the number of conductors to be connected together

(v) the temperature attained by the terminals in normal service such that the effectiveness of the insulation of the conductors connected to them is not impaired

(vi) where a soldered connection is used the design shall take account of creep, mechanical stress and temperature rise under fault current conditions

(vii) the provision of adequate locking arrangements in situations subject to vibration or thermal cycling.

Regulation 526-04-01 (part of)

Except for the following, every connection and joint shall be accessible for inspection, testing and maintenance:

(iii) a joint made by welding, soldering, brazing or compression tool.

Moulded connector strips and blocks

Care must be taken to ensure a proper connection is made when moulded connector strips and blocks are used.

Snag 45

A poor connection at a moulded connector block will result in overheating and a risk of fire.

Common problems seen with moulded connector strips and blocks include:

- Inferior quality connectors with problems such as:
  - insufficient thickness of insulation
  - substandard insulation material
  - poor quality screwed connections

- Use of an incorrect size of connector strip resulting in a loose connection

- Stripping back insufficient insulation and screwing down on to the insulation resulting in an electrically poor joint

- Overtightening screws severing one or more strands of the cable resulting in a poor joint both electrically and mechanically

- Failure to properly enclose the connection, where required. It is not acceptable to merely tape up an exposed connector block when installing a luminaire in a loft, for example

- The connector block not being accessible for inspection, testing and maintenance.

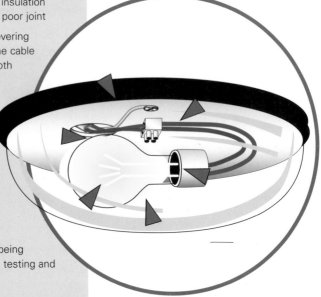

Wiring Systems

snags and solutions © NICEIC

Solution

Insulating material

Moulded connector strips and blocks are often used to make connections between cables in joint boxes and elsewhere. These strips or blocks are only acceptable if the insulating portion is of a suitable material. Far too much use is made of connectors shrouded in materials with a relatively low melting point, particularly for connecting ceiling-mounted luminaires. Connectors should be chosen with care so that they will withstand the maximum temperature likely to occur in the enclosure in which they are used. Clearly, a connector shrouded in pvc (thermoplastic) is suitable for jointing pvc-insulated cables (thermoplastic).

Connectors shrouded in thermosetting plastic or porcelain may be necessary under conditions of elevated temperature. Thermoplastic materials having a lower melting point than pvc or poorer combustibility characteristics should not be employed, even though the insulation resistance characteristics might be superior.

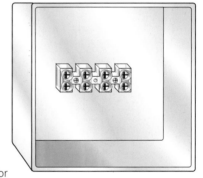

Where cables having insulation of dissimilar characteristics are joined, for example general purpose pvc and 150°C rubber, the insulation of the block or strip must be compatible with the insulating material with the higher temperature rating of the two insulating materials.

Connections must be enclosed.

The connection(s) must be properly enclosed as required by Regulation 526-03-02.

Connections must be accessible.

Every connection and joint made by a screwed moulded connector block must be accessible (Regulation 526-04-01 refers).

Connections must be properly made

Regulations 133-01-04, 526-01-01 and 526-02-01 refer.

Further recommendations include:

- Moulded connector blocks should, where possible, be fixed in position.

- In situations where a high level of heat may be a problem, for example a luminaire fitted with a tungsten filament lamp, porcelain connector blocks may need to be employed.

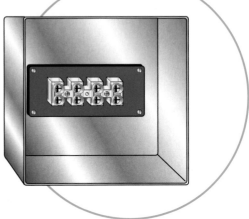

- Where a moulded connector block is to be fitted in a metal enclosure, a suggestion is to mount the block on a sheet of insulating material.

- One practice occasionally encountered is the securing of both conductors under both screws of the moulded connector block - as shown in the diagram. There is no particular problem with this practice, in fact, it could be argued that a more secure connection can be effected.

Regulation 133-01-04

Every electrical joint and connection shall be of proper construction as regards conductance, insulation, mechanical strength and protection.

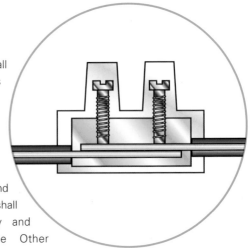

Regulation 526-01-01

Every connection between conductors and between a conductor and equipment shall provide durable electrical continuity and adequate mechanical strength (see Other mechanical stresses, Regulation 522-08).

Regulation 526-02-01

The selection of the means of connection shall take account, as appropriate, of the following:

(i)   the material of the conductor and its insulation

(ii) the number and shape of the wires forming the conductor

(iii) the cross-sectional area of the conductor

(iv) the number of conductors to be connected together

(v)   the temperature attained by the terminals in normal service such that the effectiveness of the insulation of the conductors connected to them is not impaired

(vi) where a soldered connection is used the design shall take account of creep, mechanical stress and temperature rise under fault current conditions

(vii) the provision of adequate locking arrangements in situations subject to vibration or thermal cycling.

Regulation 526-03-02

Every termination and joint in a live conductor or a PEN conductor shall be made within one of the following or a combination thereof:

(i)   a suitable accessory complying with the appropriate British Standard

(ii) an equipment enclosure complying with the appropriate British Standard

(iii) a suitable enclosure of material complying with the relevant glow-wire test requirements of BS 6458-2.1

(iv) an enclosure formed or completed with building material considered to be non-combustible when tested to BS 476-4

(v)   an enclosure formed or completed by part of the building structure, having the ignitability characteristic 'P' as specified in BS 476 Part 5.

Regulation 526-04-01 (summary)

(With permitted exceptions) every connection and joint shall be accessible for inspection, testing and maintenance. *(See Regulation for full details)*

Cable loops at motors

Unsupported loops of cable at motors may be subject to vibrational stress.

Snag 46

In a situation where there is vibration, for example in industrial applications, neither mineral insulated (MI) cables nor conduit should be employed as a wiring system. A commonly-encountered snag is to find an unsupported loop of MI cable which, apparently, has been provided either for anti-vibration purposes or to permit the motor to be physically adjusted to tension the drive belt. However, under some circumstances, the loop may actually be seen to vibrate considerably, particularly if its resonant frequency coincides with that of the rotating parts.

While such unsupported loops may absorb longitudinal movements of the cable, they are liable to increase the effect of axial (transverse) vibrations with consequent work-hardening of the conductors and the metal sheath or armour, leading to eventual fracture.

Sometimes the loops of cables are so large that they are susceptible to being pushed, pulled, twisted or trodden on.

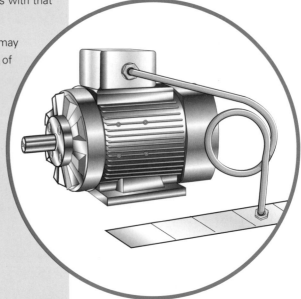

Solution

An assessment has to be made of the conditions of vibration (amongst other external influences) to which each item of equipment of an installation is likely to be exposed (Regulation 300-01-01 refers). Such an assessment involves identifying the sources and likely severity of vibration. Sources of vibration, such as machinery or parts of the building structure through which vibration may be transmitted to the electrical installation, are normally readily identifiable. The severity of vibration is taken into account in the requirements of BS 7671 by the use of three classifications:

- Low severity (code AH1) - such as may apply in household and similar environments where the effects of vibration are generally negligible

- Medium severity (code AH2) - such as may apply in usual industrial environments

- High severity (code AH3) - such as may apply in severe industrial environments

BS 7671 requires that parts of an installation affected by vibration are selected and erected to be suitable for such conditions. Otherwise vibration may cause damage to the installation, for example by causing fixings and electrical connections to become loose, or to work-harden, and fail - possibly leading to danger or failure of equipment to function correctly.

The effects of vibration must be avoided (Regulation 522-07-01 refers) and large loops of cable that are susceptible to being pushed, pulled, twisted or trodden on would be a departure from Regulations 522-08-05, 526-01-01 and 543-03-01 relating to the avoidance of mechanical damage to cables and protective conductors.

There is a growing tendency to avoid the use of flexible conduit for the final connection to an electric motor and instead use an armoured or mineral insulated cable. The use of flexible conduit used to be normal practice when most industrial installations were carried out in steel conduit or, for larger machines, in paper-insulated lead-sheathed cables.

An armoured cable (XLPE/SWA/PVC) may be suitable for the supply cable to a motor, but not where the vibration is severe. Where there is considerable vibration, neither mineral insulated cable nor a steel conduit system should be selected unless there are environmental reasons for so doing. The problem of the final connection to the motor which may need to be moved for belt adjustment needs to be considered.

One solution is to terminate the fixed wiring at a connection box and to make the final connection by means of a braided flexible cable or cord or a pliable or flexible conduit, giving due consideration to the risk of mechanical damage and that the flexible conduit must not be used as a protective conductor (Regulation 543-02-01 refers).

It should be noted that there is no reason why a sufficient length of cable should not be included to allow the removal and subsequent reinstallation of a motor. However, any loop of cable for this purpose should be adequately supported and arranged so that it will not be subject to mechanical damage from vibration or any other cause

In situations of severe vibration of the equipment to which connections are to be made, for instance screens or vibrators in process plant, it may not be possible to provide a flexible cable which will withstand indefinitely the stress imposed on it. In such circumstances, the owner of the installation should be informed that it is a maintenance requirement to change the flexible cable at regular and possibly frequent intervals.

Fixings, glands and terminals. Fixings associated with cables, conduits, cable trays or other parts of a wiring system where it is judged that vibration might loosen such fixings should be provided with adequate locking arrangements, such as shakeproof washers or self-locking nuts. Locking arrangements should also be provided at glands of cables and flexible conduits where connecting to equipment that is subject to vibration. Terminals that are subject to vibration should be provided with adequate locking arrangements, such as shakeproof washers or self-locking nuts (Regulation 526-02-01 (vii) refers).

Regulation 300-01-01 (part of)

An assessment shall be made of the following characteristics of the installation in accordance with the chapters indicated:

    (ii) the external influences to which it is to be exposed (Chapter 32).

Regulation 522-07-01

A wiring system supported by, or fixed to, a structure or equipment subject
to vibration of medium severity (AH2) or high severity (AH3) shall be suitable for the
conditions and in particular shall employ cable with fixings and connections suitable
for such a situation.

Regulation 522-08-05

Every cable or conductor or conductor used as fixed wiring shall be supported in such
a way that it is not exposed to undue mechanical strain and so that there is no
appreciable mechanical strain on the terminations of the conductors, account being
taken of mechanical strain imposed by the supported weight of the cable or
conductor itself.

Regulation 526-01-01

Every connection between conductors and between a conductor and equipment
shall provide durable electrical continuity and adequate mechanical strength (see
Other mechanical stresses, Regulation 522-08).

Regulation 526-02-01 (part of)

The selection of the means of connection should take account, as appropriate, of the
following:

   (vii) the provision of adequate locking arrangements in situation subject to
       vibration or thermal cycling.

Regulation 543-02-01 (part of)

Flexible or piable conduit shall not be selected as a protective conductor.

Regulation 543-03-01

A protective conductor shall be suitably protected against mechanical and chemical
deterioration and electrodynamic effects.

---

snags and solutions © NICEIC

Green goo

Green goo is a phenomena sometimes encountered in electrical installations constructed in the late 1960s.

Snag 47

Unsightly green slime can occur in switch and socket-outlet boxes. It is understood that this phenomenon is most prevalent where pvc cables manufactured between 1965 and 1971 have been used.

The green slime, or green goo, is degraded di-isoctyl phthalate and is considered to result from a chemical reaction between the plasticiser of the insulation and the copper conductor in the pvc cable. Between 1965 and 1971 the temperature performance of pvc was uprated by the inclusion of an anti-oxidant into the pvc compound. An unappreciated side effect was that the anti-oxidant encouraged production of the exudate.

There is evidence to suggest that high ambient temperatures accelerate the process. The exudate is of low flammability and low toxicity. Although unsightly, it does not reduce the electrical integrity of the conductor or the insulation. However, the exudate may have detrimental effects on both accessories (in appearance and functionality terms) and their surrounding decorative finishes.

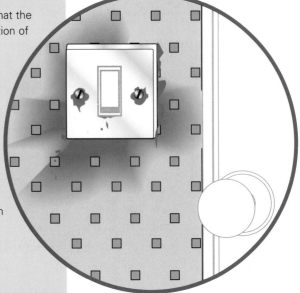

Solution

Unfortunately, where an installation is seriously affected by this deficiency, the only practicable solution is to rewire the premises and replace any damaged electrical equipment.

There are possible Health and Safety issues of retaining, working with and the disposal of contaminated wiring and accessories. Deposits of the product must not be permitted to be exposed for casual contact, particularly in areas accessible to children.

In cases where a property is to be completely rewired, redundant materials should be disconnected and removed from site. Di-isoctyl phthalate is a toxic substance and suitable protective clothing should be worn when handling waste materials. Special attention should be paid to hygiene when working on contaminated installations. Waste should be disposed of in suitable labelled containers and to registered Waste Disposal Contractors. The NICEIC strongly recommends that advice is sought from the Health and Safety Executive as to appropriate action when dealing with installations so affected.

Electromagnetic effects at ferrous enclosures

The conductors of an a.c. circuit entering a steel enclosure must not be separated by ferromagnetic material.

Snag 48

The conductors of an a.c. circuit entering a metal enclosure must not be separated by ferromagnetic material (e.g. the steel body of the enclosure or a steel gland plate) unless precautions are taken to minimize the effects of eddy currents.

The conductors in a steel conduit wiring system must be arranged so that the phase conductor(s), the neutral conductor and the circuit protective conductor are all contained within the same enclosure or, once again, eddy currents will result.

Eddy currents result in heating and, in extreme cases, to an audible hum (induction hum).

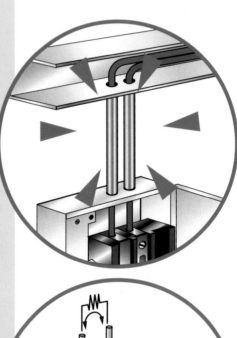

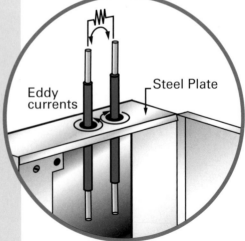

Eddy currents

Steel Plate

Solution

The conductors of an a.c. circuit in steel conduit must be run together. If this is not possible, one solution is to employ a non-ferrous enclosure.

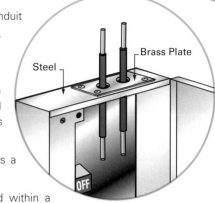

Conductors entering such an enclosure must not be separated by ferrous material unless precautions, such as providing slots between the conductors, are taken.

Alternatively a non-ferrous material such as a brass gland plate may be employed.

The conductors of an a.c. circuit installed within a ferromagnetic enclosure must be arranged so that the conductors of all phases, and the neutral conductor (if any) and the appropriate protective conductor of each circuit are contained in the same enclosure. Regulation 521-02-01 refers.

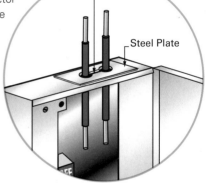

Regulation 521-02-01

Single-core cables armoured with steel wire or tape shall not be used for a.c. circuits. Conductors of a.c. circuits installed in ferromagnetic enclosures shall be arranged so that the conductors of all phases and the neutral conductor (if any) and the appropriate protective conductor of each circuit are contained in the same enclosure.

Where such conductors enter a ferrous enclosure they shall be arranged so that the conductors are not individually surrounded by a ferrous material, or other provisions shall be made to prevent eddy (induced) currents.

Slotted trunking and ducting

Slotted trunking or ducting is primarily intended for panel wiring.

Snag 49

Semi-enclosed or slotted trunking or ducting does not satisfy the requirements for enclosure of **non-sheathed cables** set out in Regulation 521-07-03 and must not be used for installation work.

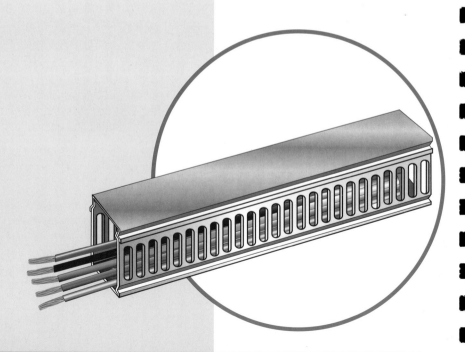

Solution

Slotted trunking or ducting is primarily intended for panel wiring and telecommunications applications and should not be used for installation work except for containing sheathed cables.

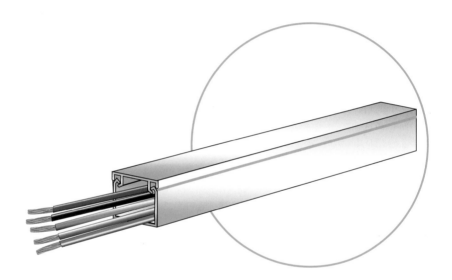

Regulation 521-07-03 (part of)

Non-sheathed cables for fixed wiring shall be enclosed in conduit, ducting or trunking. This regulation does not apply to a protective conductor complying with Section 543 of the Regulations.

Temperature rise in mineral insulated cables

Temperature rises in mineral insulated metal sheathed (MIMS) cables can be high enough to cause burns and deterioration of the insulation of other equipment such as accessories or pvc cables with which they may be in contact.

Snag 50

A bare mineral insulated cable, under full load conditions, is permitted to have a sheath temperature of up to 105 °C. (Table 4J2A of BS 7671 refers).

Use of the higher ratings given in Table 4J2A for a bare MIMS cable could result in the risk of burns, fires, other injurious effects and damage to equipment such as an accessory that is not suitably rated.

For example, where a MIMS cable is installed adjacent to an ordinary pvc cable, care must be taken that the permitted temperature rise in the MIMS cable is not so high as to cause deterioration in the insulation of the pvc cable. This applies to MIMS cables bunched in air with pvc-insulated and sheathed cables as well as to MIMS and pvc-insulated cables installed together in trunking.

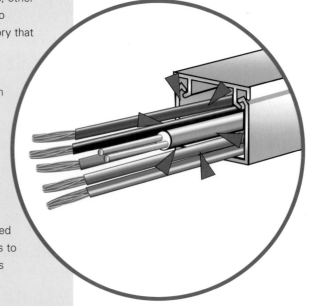

Solution

If the MIMS cables are loaded at currents no greater than those shown in Tables 4J1A (sheath operating temperature 70 °C), and the appropriate rating factors for ambient temperature and grouping are taken into account, no problems are likely to arise.

Alternatively, bare MIMS cables which are likely to operate at temperatures greater than 70 °C should be installed in such a manner that they

- cannot be touched, and

- are segregated from other cables, and

- are terminated into equipment suitably rated for such elevated temperatures.

(Regulation 130-03-02 refers).

Regulation 130-03-02

Persons, fixed equipment and fixed materials adjacent to electrical equipment shall be protected against harmful effects of heat or thermal radiation emitted by electrical equipment, particularly the following consequences:

(i) combustion, ignition, or degradation of materials

(ii) risk of burns

(iii) impairment of the safe function of installed equipment.

Electrical equipment shall not present a fire hazard to adjacent materials.

Switch drop cables

Switch drop cables must be properly identified.

Snag 51

Where a cable such as a flat twin and earth cable is used as a switch drop cable, both insulated conductors are employed as line or phase conductors and must be identified accordingly.

Failure to correctly identify conductors can lead to the risk of electric shock for electricians repairing, modifying, altering or extending the installation at a future date.

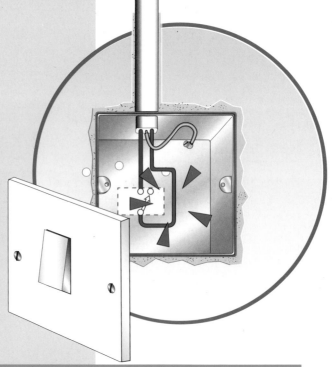

Solution

The conductor with blue insulation in a flat twin and earth cable may be used as a switched phase conductor but must be properly identified at its terminations.

Cables such as flat 'twin and earth' cable used for connecting between a ceiling rose and a plate switch must be suitably identified at each termination. This will normally be accomplished by fitting a brown sleeve to the blue conductor.

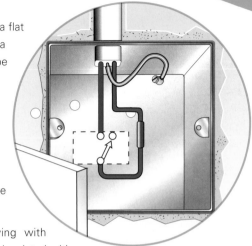

Flat twin and earth cable complying with BS 6004: 1990, and having each core insulated with brown-coloured pvc, may be made available. There are evident advantages in using 'twin brown' cable for switch drops, in that it avoids the necessity of having to mark up blue cores with brown sleeves, and helps easy recognition of switch drop cables at ceiling rose or luminaire positions.

Regulation 514-04-04

Other conductors shall be identified by colour in accordance with Table 51.

TABLE 51 (part of)

Function	Colour identification
Phase of single-phase circuit	Brown

Identification of conductors in a swa cable

Where a 3-core steel wire armoured (swa) cable is selected for use in a single-phase circuit, the conductors must be properly identified.

Snag 52

Failure to properly identify the cores of a 3-core swa cable could present difficulties for an electrician carrying out maintenance or modification work in the future.

Solution

Every single-core non-flexible cable and every core of non-flexible cable for use as fixed wiring shall be identifiable, at its terminations and preferably throughout its length, by an appropriate method identified in Regulation 514-03-01.

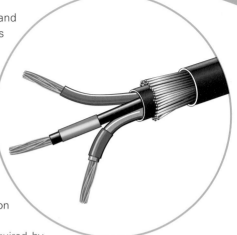

Regulation 514-03-01

Except where identification is not required by Regulation 514-06, cores of cables shall be identified by:

   (i) colour as required by Regulation 514-04 and/or

   (ii) lettering and/or numbering as required by Regulation 514-05.

Regulation 514-04-01

Where a circuit includes a neutral or mid-point conductor identified by colour, the colour used shall be blue.

Regulation 514-04-02 (part of)

The bi-colour combination green-and-yellow shall be used exclusively for identification of a protective conductor and this combination shall not be used for any other purpose.

Regulation 514-04-04

Other conductors shall be identified by colour in accordance with Table 51.

Table 51 Identification of conductors (part of)

a.c. power circuit (including lighting circuits)	Alphanumeric	Colour
Phase of single-phase circuit	L	Brown
Neutral of single- or three-phase circuit	N	Blue

Conductors must be correctly identified

Conductors must be correctly identified by colour or alphanumerically to avoid confusion when the installation is repaired, extended or modified at a later date.

Snag 53

Where a conductor is not correctly identified, a dangerous trap can easily be created for an electrician carrying out maintenance or modification work in the future.

Conductors colour coded green-and-yellow must not be used for any other purpose.

An instance has been recently encountered of a conductor with green-and-yellow insulation being oversleeved in brown and used as the switched live conductor in a supply to an extract fan incorporating a timer for a windowless bathroom.

A similar example can occur with a central heating systems where a 3-core flexible cord is taken to a cylinder thermostat of a type that does not require earthing and the green-and-yellow core of the cord is misused as a switch-wire.

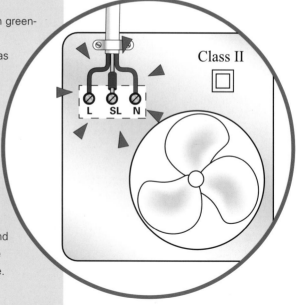

Class II

L   SL   N

Solution

The colour combination green-and-yellow must only be used for a protective conductor. (Regulation 514-04-02 refers).

In the two snags given, the cable must be replaced.

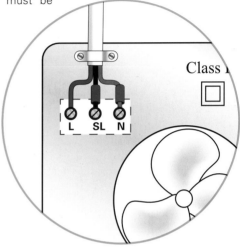

Regulation 514-04-02 (part of)

The bi-colour combination green-and-yellow shall be used exclusively for identification of a protective conductor and this combination shall not be used for any other purpose.

Safety with flexible cords

Electric hedge cutters and lawnmowers are easily able to cut through the supply cord

Snag 54

Hedge cutters and lawnmowers have sharp blades and rapidly moving parts capable of cutting through electric cables as easily as a hedge or grass. The risk of electric shock from the exposed live conductors is high and is further increased because the person is likely to be in contact with Earth.

Solution

For safety:

- RCD protection must be provided for the supply to portable equipment outdoors (Regulations 471-16-01, 471-16-02 and 412-06-02 refer)

- Check that the RCD is working by pressing the 'test' button at least once every three months (Regulation 514-12-02 refers)

- Check the condition of the flexible cord, the connections and the plug before use

- Wear suitable protective clothing and footwear

- Do not cut the hedge or the grass in wet conditions. Keep the cord clear of water or puddles

- When cutting, keep the cable well clear of the cutting area

- Before clearing blockages or carrying out maintenance, unplug the hedge cutter or lawnmower and wait for the blades to stop moving

- Keep children away from the area

- Store equipment in a dry place and safely out of reach of children.

Courtesy of Legrand Electric Ltd

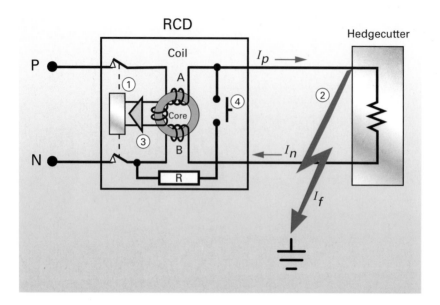

P =	Phase	I_p = Phase current	① = Trip relay
N =	Neutral	I_n = Neutral current	② = Earth Fault
E =	Earth	I_f = Earth fault current	③ = Amplifier
R =	Resistor in test circuit		④ = Test push button

In the event of a fault current (I_f) flowing to earth as shown above, I_p will not equal I_n creating an inbalance in the core of the RCD. Under these conditions the RCD is arranged to operate and disconnect the supply.

Regulation 412-06-02 (part of)

(ii) the residual current device shall have a rated residual operating current ($I_{\Delta n}$) not exceeding 30 mA and an operating time not exceeding 40 ms at a residual current of 5 $I_{\Delta n}$, as provided by BS 4293, BS 7071, BS 7288, BS EN 61008-1 or BS EN 61009-1.

Regulation 471-16-01 (part of)

A socket-outlet rated at 32 A or less which may reasonably be expected to supply portable equipment for use outdoors shall be provided with supplementary protection to reduce the risk associated with direct contact by means of a residual current device having the characteristics specified in Regulation 412-06-02(ii).

Regulation 471-16-02

Except where one or more of the protective measures specified in items (i) to (iii) of Regulation 471-16-01 are applied in accordance with the corresponding regulations stated therein, a circuit supplying portable equipment for use outdoors, connected other than through a socket-outlet by means of flexible cable or cord having a current-carrying capacity of 32 A or less, shall be provided with supplementary protection to reduce the risk associated with direct contact by means of a residual current device having the characteristics specified in Regulation 412-06-02(ii).

Regulation 514-12-02 (part of)

Where an installation incorporates a residual current device a notice shall be fixed in a prominent position at or near the origin of the installation.

(See regulation for full details which include the required size of the characters of the notice)

> **This installation, or part of it, is protected by a device which automatically switches off the supply if an earth fault develops. Test quarterly by pressing the button marked 'T' or 'Test'. The device should switch off the supply and should then be switched on to restore the supply. If the device does not switch off the supply when the button is pressed, seek expert advice.**
>
>

Cables on construction sites

Cables on construction sites can suffer damage unless adequate precautions are taken

Snag 55

The risk of danger from electrical hazards on a construction or demolition site can be high due to accidental damage of cables and the fact that cables may be trailing. Working conditions on construction sites are generally difficult and parts of the electrical installation may be in the open and subject to the prevailing weather conditions.

Solution

BS 7671 recognizes the risk of danger from electrical hazards on construction and demolition sites and gives both general requirements and, in Section 604, *Construction Site Installations* additional requirements that supplement or modify the general requirements. Account should also be taken of the guidance given in BS 7375: *Code of practice for distribution of electricity on construction and building sites*.

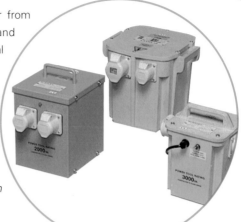

For the purposes of applying the supplementary requirements of Section 604 of BS 7671, construction site installations are limited to:

- the assembly comprising the main switchgear and the main protective devices, and
- the installation on the load side of this assembly, which is considered as a movable installation. The assembly comprising the main switchgear and main protective devices is considered to be the interface between the supply system and the construction site installation, and the place where such an assembly is located is the origin of the installation.

The movable part of the installation comprises equipment such as:

- 400 V 3-phase compressors and transformer assemblies,
- 230 V tower flood lighting,
- 110 V hand tools, for example power drills and angle grinders,
- 110 V lighting, for example fluorescent and festoon type lighting.

In many cases, hand tools will present the greatest risk of electric shock.

The use of the Automatic Disconnection and Reduced Low Voltage (ADRLV) system on construction sites has made a major contribution to construction and demolition site electrical safety.

The maximum permitted nominal voltages for typical applications on construction sites are listed in the Table.

Maximum nominal supply voltage a.c. rms.	Application
SELV, 50 V	Portable hand lamps in confined or damp locations
110 V, 1-phase, centre point earthed	Reduced low voltage system Portable hand lamps for general use Portable hand-held tools and local lighting up to 2 kW
110 V, 3-phase, star point earthed	Reduced low voltage system Portable hand-held tools and local lighting up to 2 kW Small mobile plant, up to 3.75 kW
230 V, 1-phase	Fixed floodlighting
400 V, 3-phase	Fixed and movable equipment, above 3.75 kW

Note that where necessary, a high voltage supply such as 3.3 kV or 11 kV may be used for electrical equipment having a large power consumption.

Wiring systems used on construction sites fall into two categories: those which are fixed and those that are likely to be moved in normal use. Fixed wiring on a construction site will normally use steel-wire armoured (SWA) cables. Cables likely to be frequently moved in normal use must be flexible cables, and steel-wire armoured cables are not considered to be flexible cables.

Recommendations for safety from BS 7375 and other industry guidance includes:

Cables

Cable should be routed away from operations, as far as is practicable, should not be a hazard to personnel, and should be kept clear of walkways, ladders and piped services. Cables that are likely to be frequently moved should be of the flexible type.

Cables with voltages to earth between 12 V and 63.5 V. Every fixed or flexible cable which has a voltage to earth of greater than 12 V but not exceeding 63.5 V applied to it should be of a type which is insulated and sheathed. Such a cable, however, does not need necessarily to be of the metal sheathed and/or armoured type, although this type of cable may be used.

Cables with voltages to earth greater than 63.5 V. Every fixed or flexible cable which may normally have a voltage to earth in excess of 63.5 V applied to it should be of a type having a metal sheath such as a braid and/or an armour. Note that supplies from welding transformers to welding electrodes are exempt from these recommendations.

Metal sheathed and/or armoured cables. As in all cases, the metal sheath, braid or armour of a cable must be continuously and effectively earthed.

Cables with protective conductors. Where a cable incorporates a protective conductor, the cross-sectional area of the protective conductor should not be less than that of the largest associated phase conductor.

Flexible cables must have a protective conductor core. Every flexible cable must have a protective conductor core regardless of whether it is metal sheathed or braided and/or armoured. The reason for this recommendation is to ensure the function of the protective conductor is not lost by misuse such as the cable armour being pulled out of a gland.

Types of flexible cable permitted. Section 604 of BS 7671 defines the installation on the load side of the main switchgear and the main protective devices to be the movable installation and therefore only makes reference to flexible cables.

For reduced low voltage systems, Regulation 604-10-03 requires the use of low temperature 300/500 V thermoplastic (pvc) type, or equivalent.

For applications where the voltage exceeds reduced low voltage, up to and including 400 V, the same regulation requires the use of 450/750 V flexible cable, type H07 RN-F, or equivalent.

Other recommendations for flexible cables include:

- Cable insulation material should be suitable for the lowest ambient temperature expected on the site and the outer sheath should be water, oil, impact and abrasion resistant.

- General purpose pvc insulated cables conforming to BS 6004 are not acceptable on a construction site for use in locations where a flexible cable or cord is required.

- The conductor cross-sectional area should not be less than 1.5 mm^2.

Cable glands

Cable glands play an important role in the safety of the construction site installation.

Recommendations for cable glands include:

- Suitable glands must be employed which are suitable for both the environment and the size and type of cable. Shrouds, seals, IP washers and earth tag washers may be required.

- Glands must be correctly fitted and sufficiently tightened. Serrated lock washers may be necessary.

- Glands should be kept free from undue strain. Switchgear used on a construction site should comply with BS 4363 which requires adequate provision be made for anchoring incoming and outgoing cables, and such facilities must be used to protect the cable terminations from the effects of movement. Regulation 522-08 of BS 7671 gives applicable requirements relating to mechanical stresses on cables, conductors and their terminations.

- Connection to earth for the armouring or braiding will generally be provided by the cable gland. This will be achieved by the proper assembly of the gland together with an earth tag washer, nut, bolt, washers and a short length of suitably-sized copper protective conductor connected from the earth tag washer to the earthing terminal within the switchgear, distribution equipment or current-using equipment. On no account should an earthing and bonding clamp to BS 951, or other similar device, be applied to the metal sheath or armouring for this or any other purpose. Such misuse of the clamp is likely to damage the cable and would be considered unreliable for earthing purposes.

Protection of cables on site

snag **55**

Cables installed across a site road or walkway. Cables must not
be installed across a site road or walkway unless adequate protection of the
cable against mechanical damage is provided (Regulation 604-10-02).

Buried cables. Precautions must be taken to avoid damage to, or accidental contact
with, underground cables. Except where installed in a conduit or duct which provides
equivalent protection against mechanical damage, where a cable is directly buried in
the ground the cable must either be of a type incorporating an earthed metal sheath
or armour or both suitable for use as a protective conductor or be of insulated
concentric construction. A buried cable must be laid at sufficient depth to avoid being
damaged by any reasonably foreseeable disturbance of the ground. A warning of the
presence of a buried cable is to be given in the form of cable tiles, or suitably marked
tape, laid above the cable between the cable and the surface of the ground. The
routes of buried cables should be identified by means of cable markers at intervals
along the route and records of the location of such cable, using maps or plans
showing its route and depth, should be made and kept. (Regulation 522-06-03 gives
requirements for buried cables). *(See Snag 11)*.

Overhead cables. Precautions must be taken to avoid damage to, or accidental
contact with, overhead cables which should, ideally, be made dead or rerouted before
work starts. If this is not possible, precautions should be put in place to ensure they
are not approached or disturbed.

Alternative sources of energy

Finally, it must not be forgotten that where electrical risks are particularly high, such
as in waterlogged conditions on construction sites, alternatives sources of energy
such as battery-powered or air-powered tools may significantly reduce the risks of
electrical dangers or eliminate them altogether

Further information

Further information on electrical safety on construction sites is given in the NICEIC Technical Manual in Topic S205-29 *Construction sites – General*.

Useful guidance is given in BS 7375: *Code of practice for distribution of electricity on construction and building sites*.

Further information on protection of cables on construction sites is given in the HSE publications.

- HS(G) 6, GS6 *Avoidance of danger from overhead electric lines*,
- HS(G) 47, *Avoiding danger from underground services*, and
- HS(G) 141 (formerly GS 24), *Electrical Safety on Construction Sites*.

Regulation 604-10-02

Cable shall not be installed across a site road or a walkway unless adequate protection of the cable against mechanical damage is provided.

Regulation 604-10-03

For a reduced low voltage system, low temperature 300/500 V thermoplastic (pvc) or equivalent flexible cables shall be used. For applications exceeding the reduced low voltage system in compliance with (v) and (vi) of Regulation 604-02-02, flexible cable shall be H07 RN-F type or equivalent having 450/750 V rating and resistant to abrasion and water.

Note

(v) of Regulation 604-02-02 refers to 230 V 1-phase supply to fixed floodlighting

(vi) of Regulation 604-02-02 refers to 400 V 3-phase supplies to fixed and movable equipment above 3.75 kW.

Index by subject

A-C

snags and solutions © NICEIC